OPEN PAN SALT MAKING IN CHESHIRE

An illustrated description by Tom Lightfoot

Edited by Annelise Fielding

Lion Salt Works Trust

Research Report No. 1

Open Pan Salt Making in Cheshire

An illustrated description by Tom Lightfoot
Edited by: Annelise Fielding

Original text and illustrations by Tom Lightfoot

Series editor: Andrew Fielding

First published in September, 2000 by the Lion Salt Works Trust
Ollershaw Lane, Marston, Northwich, Cheshire CW9 6ES
http://www.lionsaltworks.co.uk

ISBN 0-9538502-1-8

Dedicated to the memory of
Lady Mary Carlisle Rochester
1921 - 2000
Founder Trustee,
Lion Salt Works Trust 1993 - 2000

Acknowledgements

The Lion Salt Works Trust thanks the Lightfoot family and George Twigg
for making the manuscript available for publication.

The Worshipful Company of Salters,
Salt Manufacturers Association,
The Manifold Trust.

Designed by Glint
http://www.glint.co.uk

Contents

Maps

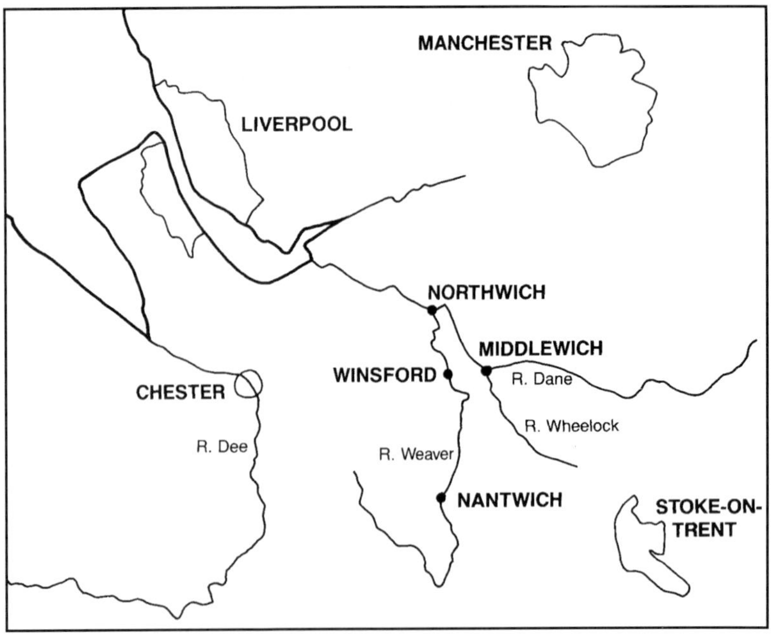

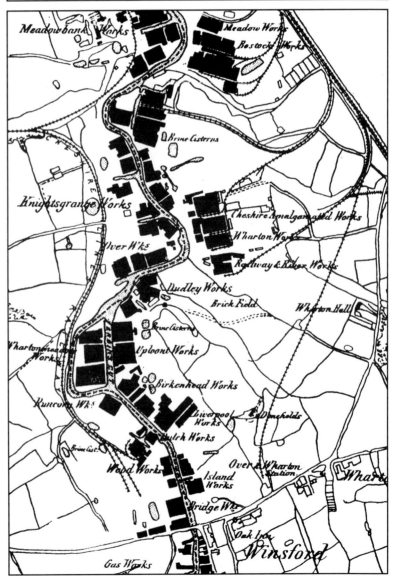

Map 1
The salt towns
of Mid-Cheshire

Map 2
Salt works formerly at
Winsford, from Calvert
(1915) Salt in Cheshire

1 Open Pan Salt Works

Before anything is said about the workers who worked on the open pan salt works some idea ought to be given of the number and names of the different works that there were on the river banks from Winsford to Newbridge.

Garner's Works were on the west bank of Winsford Bridge and covered an area from the river bank to the entrance to New Road. At the back of these works were Hamlett's Works which covered an area from New Road past the north side of Christ Church and continued behind the shops and chapel to Bakers Lane. Going down stream on the west side of the river one would next come to the Meadow Works. This was a dockyard with a floating dock built in the early 1920's, attached by a bridge. Next came the Meadow Island which had open pans but these only made common and fishery salt. It also had an engineering shop which was, with the dockyard, for the maintenance of the river craft.

Next along the river bank came the Woodend Works whose pans made light shoots which were called Lagos Salt. This was followed by the Jubilee Works whose pans made Lagos. This works also had a slipway where river craft were pulled from the river onto the bank for repair. After this came the Dairy Works whose pans made heavy shoots called hand-it salt. Next came the Vacuum Plant which was followed by the Extension Works whose pans made hand-it salt, then came the rock salt mine which was followed by the Factory Works whose pans made Lagos Salt.

Now, starting again from Winsford Bridge going down stream on the east side of the river one would come to the Birkenhead Works. This works had no lump pans, so the pans here made fishery, common and light Boston salt. Next would come the Uplooant Works whose pans made Lagos salt then the Cheshire Works where common and hand-it salt was made. This works also had a wagon shop where rail wagons were built and repaired. Along the river bank came the National Works whose pans made Lagos and common salt, then came Bostock Works which was followed a little further down the river by New Bridge Works whose pans made fishery and Lagos salt. In Winsford at this time, apart from Garner's and Hamlett's salt works who made the different types of salt, the rest of the salt works were owned by the Salt Union, later ICI.

Seddon's salt works were at Middlewich. They were open pan salt works made up of the Croxten Lane Works, Pepper Street and Wychehouse Lane Works, also Brooks Lane Works. Murgatroyd's Open Pan Salt Works was in Brooks Lane as well. Also there were open pan works at Cledford Lane, Middlewich and in Sandbach, Stafford and Lymm.

At Northwich the last open pans worked by the Salt Union were in Warrington Road. It was called Ashton's Works. The only open pans left at the time of writing of course being Thompson's at Marston. All of these made the different types of salt - common, Lagos and hand-it salt.

Of course it should be understood that on a salt works where the pans were mainly producing Lagos salt there was always quite an amount of common salt. This was because after the lump pans had finished making lumps on a Saturday, the pans as they cooled off over the week-end would make a certain amount of common salt which had to be taken out before they could begin to make lump salt again.

Of course there had to be a good supply of brine. This was got by a bore hole which was a hole bored through the ground into the stream below ground, or by digging a shaft down through the ground, some of these going down to depths of three hundred feet (90m). Pumps were then put into these bore holes or shafts and that is what was called wild brine pumping, the reason being that the brine was being pumped from the natural brine streams running underground. Nearly all the salt works had their own supply of wild brine unless of course some works were fairly close together and then one would possibly supply the other. Of course some were very close together but still had their own brine supply.

1 Brine tank

2 Wooden cistern for brine

3 Brine pump house and gallows

Some idea can be given of how the brine was stored at Winsford.

One method was to dig a hole on a high bank then bank the sides up. This was then lined with brick before the brine was put into it. These would be about 100 feet by 60 feet and 6 to 8 feet deep (30m x 18m x 3m).

Another way the brine was stored was in a wooden cistern. These were placed on brick walls about 10-15 feet high (3m x 4.5m).

The timber pump structure over the brine shaft was called the gallows because this is where the workmen hung the block and tackle for doing any repairs such as lifting broken rods from the shaft or lifting the rising-main pipe out of the brine shaft.

A number of years ago a brine pump house like this could have been seen on the east bank of the River Weaver a few minutes walk down stream from Winsford Bridge.

Now let us look at the construction of salt works. As most people know salt is very corrosive and wood is one of the building materials that stood up the best to this. So anyone going on to a salt works would find that a lot of wood was used as well as bricks.

The walls of a salt works had a brick base and a wooden wall-plate. Uprights would be mortised into the wall-plate (4). The boards would then be nailed onto the inside of the uprights, which means that the boards would be on the inside of the building and the uprights on the outside. On any salt works the outside of the buildings were always well covered with tar.

4 Wall of a saltworks

There were differences between one firm and another in the way their works were built. This could have been clearly seen if one had gone to Middlewich and seen the difference between Seddon's salt works and Murgatroyd's in Brooks Lane. These salt works were built next to each other in Brooks Lane but if one went on to Seddon's works it would have been seen that all the walls round the lump pans and also the walls round the salt warehouses or 'store-rus' were built of brick. However, if one had gone on to Murgatroyd's works they would have seen that all the walls round the lump pans apart from the brick base were all built of wood. They were also built of wood round the common pans, so there again was a difference that could have been seen round the different salt works.

The roofs were of timber construction and where they covered the lump pans, or the bigger fishery or common pans, they would always be built with the roofs open at the top, this being done to allow the steam from the boiling brine to escape. The bottom part of the roof was felted so as to give the lumpman or waller some protection from the weather while they were working along

5 Roof Covering

side the pans (5). The upper part of the roof is just plain boarding with no felt covering. Of course there were some salt works where the fishery pans had no cover over the top at all.

While we are getting some idea of the amount of timber that was used it should also be understood that all the gutterings between the roofs were timber as was the spouting round other buildings and the down spouting.

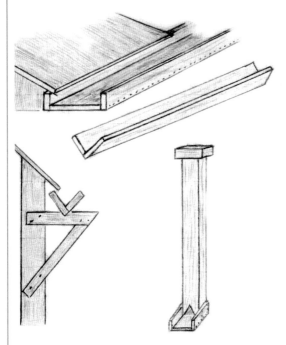

Sketch 6 will give some idea of the way rainwater was carried away from the roofs.

6a sketch shows the guttering between them.

6b shows how the spouting was made.

6c the downspout.

6d shows how the brackets were made to carry the spouting. After these had been made pitch would be melted and run along the joints and also inside the down spouting.

6a,6b,6c,6d. Gutters

The idea must not be got that all the walls were built of timber because in the hothouses where the lumps of salt finished draining and were also dried, the walls were built of bricks, the reason being that as much heat as possible had to be kept inside.

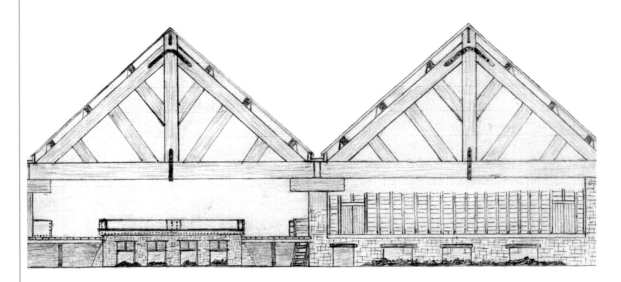

7 Roof construction

Above the hothouses there was a warehouse where the lumps were stored after they had been dried. This was called the lump room or the mill room because there was a grinding mill in this room used for grinding the salt lumps up so that the salt could be put into bags.

The roofs were fixed over the pans on timber pillars or brick pillars. Sketch 7 shows the front of the pan where the fires were put under. It also shows the hurdles on each side of the pan, the water butts or bosh as they were called, and the steps the lumpman used when going from the hurdle down to attend to the fires. This was called going down into the holes. It also shows what the front of the building looked like.

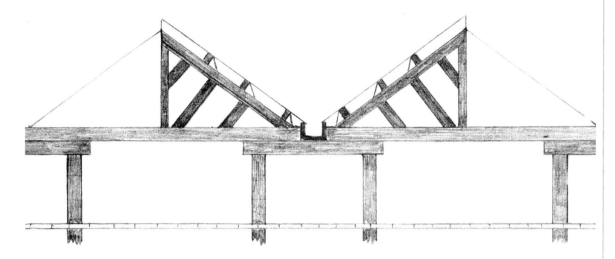

8 Roof supports

Although all the roofs were built on the same principle some of them looked a little different as is shown in Sketch 8.

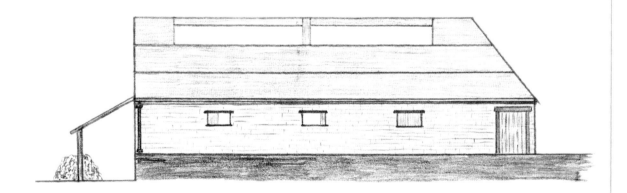

9 Outline of roof

The roof had a lean-to cover over the fire holes. When they were built like this a wooden screen was built at the front end of the pan to keep out the dust and dirt from the fire holes. Of course it should be explained that the windows did not have glass in them. They had wooden shutters that could be set to how the lumpman wanted them (10 and 11).

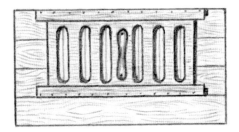 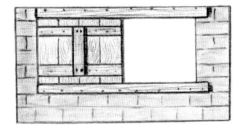

10 Window with sliding shutter with slots 11 Window with sliding shutter

It would be of some interest to look at a safety measure which was used on the ends of the roofs.

12 metal spikes on roof

Metal spikes were put into the ends of the roofs. This was so that a spar could be put across them, then a ladder could be rested against the spar, thereby making it quite simple to get to any part of the end of the roofs. These were not used in between the roofs as a ladder could be rested in the guttering. On some firms blocks of wood were fastened on instead of the spikes. The metal spikes were about four or five inches long (100-130mm) above the roof boards.

Of course this sort of thing was done when the roofs were covered with boards and then felted. In later years when the roofs had worn out many were covered with corrugated asbestos sheeting. So here again if someone had seen the roofs when they were boarded and covered with felt it made them look quite a bit different when they were covered with corrugated sheeting.

Having got some idea of the amount of timber used on a salt works there could also be seen a great amount of brickwork. If all the bricks were counted that were used in the building of the chimneys one would come to a great number.

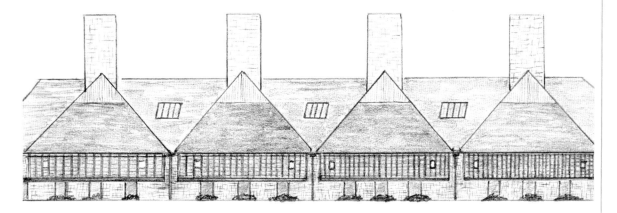

13 Pans built close together

If the number of pans were counted, and most pans had their own chimney which were around seventy to eighty feet high (21m to 24m), the amount of bricks that were used can be seen. Hamlett's at Winsford and Seddon's at Middlewich had their own brickyards.

The pans were built close together. As a rule they were built three or four together which meant they were able to build one big warehouse at the back with the hothouses underneath, this of course making a very compact works. The pans were each numbered and the area where the pans were housed was called the lump yard.

The layout of the lump pan, the hothouse and the lump room is shown as these all work in line with each other.

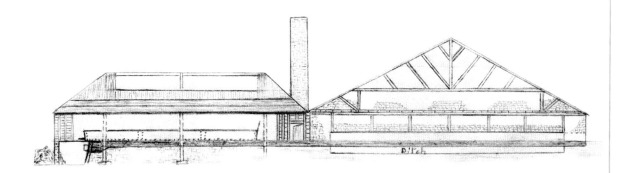

14 A long section showing the layout of lump pan

Sketch 14 shows the flue going from the fires into the hothouse. It also shows how the ditch is on a lower level than the hothouse floor with the lump room above the hothouse.

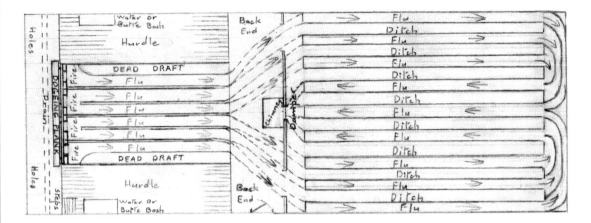

15 A plan showing the position of flues under the pan and hothouse

Sketch 15 shows the position of the pan, the flues under the pan and the way the ditches and flues are laid out in the hothouse. It shows how the hot gases travelling from the pan through the flues went through the outside flues, returning through the centre flues to the chimney. It also shows the hurdles on each side of the pan, the water butts or bosh and the dodging plank, which was hung on the outside of the rim plate across the front of the pan. The steps are also shown which lead from the hurdle down to the holes, this being the name of the place where the fires were attended to.

Let us now look at the lump pan from another angle so as to get a better idea what it looked like.

The lump pan was made of steel plates riveted together (16). There was no difference in construction between the lump pan and the common or fishery pan, the only difference being in the size, the lump pan being approximately forty feet long (12m) and the common or fishery salt pans being approximately seventy to eighty feet long by twenty wide (24m x 6m).

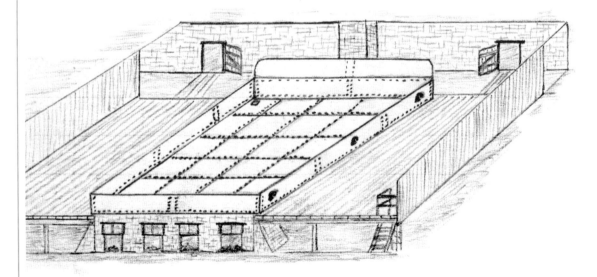

16 The lump pan from another angle

They had the same depth of about eighteen inches (460mm). It should be noticed from the sketch (16) that the pan is raised up from the ground. The pan itself lay on brick walls about six to seven feet high (1.8-2.1m). This was done so as to give room at the front to put the fire grates under. As a rule there were four fires under each pan which were coal fired and were attended to by the lumpman. When the pan was lowered onto the walls this was called dropping the pan. It was always set so that the front of the pan (the front being where the fires were) was always slightly higher than the back end of the pan.

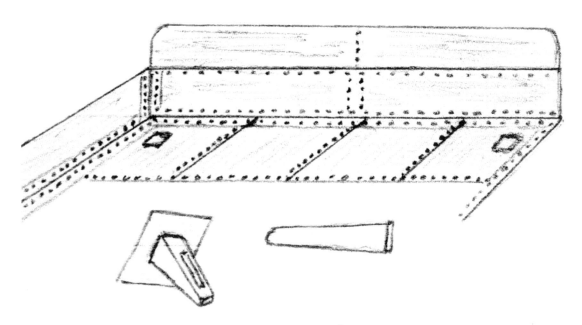

17 Cotter patches, cotter holes, cotter pin

The reason for this was that in the bottom of the pan at the back end in each corner were two holes which were used for emptying the pan. These were called cotter holes. These were covered by the cotter patches before the pan was filled.

The cotter pin was used to hold the patch down. When the cotter patch was put on, pieces of cloth were put on the patch, thick lime was then put round the hole and the patch was then put on, the cotter pin put in and hammered tight.

On each side and level with the bottom of the pan was the part where the lumpman worked when he was filling his tubs with salt. This was called the hurdle. It was built of wooden planks laid alongside each other and nailed down to cross-beams (18).

When the planks were laid down a space was left between each one to provide easy drainage, the space between being about one eighth inch (3mm).

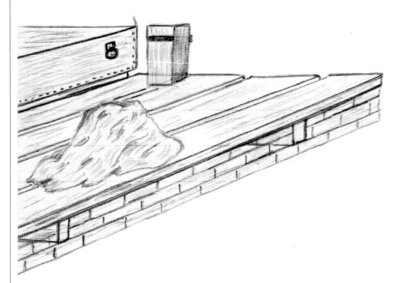

18 The hurdle alongside the pan

When the tubs, filled with salt, were put on the hurdle the brine from them would drain away through the space between the planks. This would also happen if loose salt was put on.

A space can be seen between the bottom of the pan and the hurdle. This was a safety measure so that the lumpman could get the toe of his clog under the pan and this was called toe room. The toe going under the pan allowed the lumpman to get his leg against the side of the pan when he was lifting the salt out.

There would be a wooden water butt on each hurdle, which meant that there would be two butts to each pan. Of course, they were not all of wood, some were made of steel plates riveted together. The size of these butts was about four foot long by two foot wide by two feet deep (1.2m x 0.6m x 0.6m).

They were called the bosh by the lumpman (19).

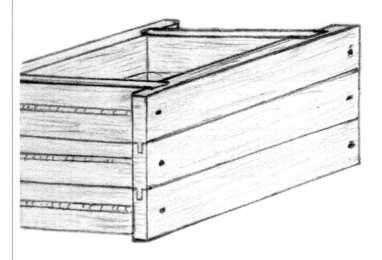

19 Water butt

There were some differences from works to works in the way the hurdles were built.

20 Pan above the hurdle

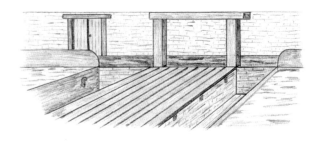

21 Pan below the hurdle

Sketch 20 shows a pan which had been built above the level of the hurdle. A low platform was built alongside it so that the waller was able to draw the salt out of the pan. This could have been seen on one of the common pans at the Meadow Works at Winsford.

Sketch 21 shows a pan which had been built below the level of the hurdle. It shows the space that was left lower than the hurdle and level with the bottom of the pan in which the waller could stand to draw salt from the pan. This could have been seen at the common pans at Seddon's Brooks Lane Works at Middlewich.

There was a raised plate at the back of the pan called the splash plate. This was put on so that if anyone was working or walking past the end of the pan when the lumpman was raking the salt to the side, this plate was to prevent them getting splashed with hot brine (22). However, one could have gone to another works and seen pans with a splash plate at both ends.

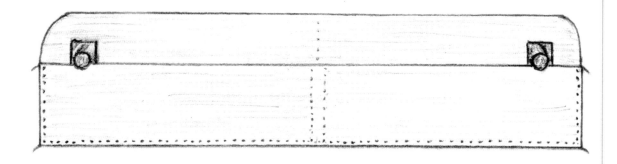

22 Splash plate at front of pan

The splash plate at the front end of a pan had holes cut into it to allow the brine feed to enter the pan (22).

Also on the lump pan was a type of metal shelf. These were put on each side of the pan on the inside. They were used to put the salt tubs on while they were being filled with salt. These were called the dogs (23).

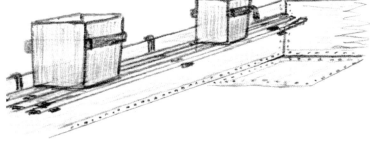

23 The dogs hanging inside the pan with the tubs on

The reason the tubs were filled like this was that when the salt was lifted out of the pan it would still be saturated with hot brine so that when the salt was put into the tub the hot brine would drain through the bottom of the tub back into the pan. If this had not been done and the tubs had been filled on the hurdle, the hot brine would have gone to waste, lowering the level of hot brine in the pan. If the level of hot brine had got too low, too great an amount of cold brine would have had to be run in and this would stop the pan making salt as it should.

The dodging plank was one long or two shorter planks hung across the front of the pan on the outside (24). This plank was used by the lumpman if any salt dropped onto the plate over the fires causing scale to form. The dodging plank could then be used by the lumpman to stand on when he used his dodging hammer to break the scale that had formed. However this did not happen very often (25). The head was of rounded steel about eighteen inches long (460mm) and the shaft about nine feet long (2.75m).

24 Dodging plank across the front of the pan

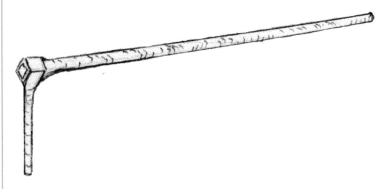

25 Dodging hammer

On another works there might not be a dodging plank on any pan. The reason being that some firms had a wooden platform built at the front end of the pan which covered the fire holes down below. The name that was given to this platform was the caboosh (26).

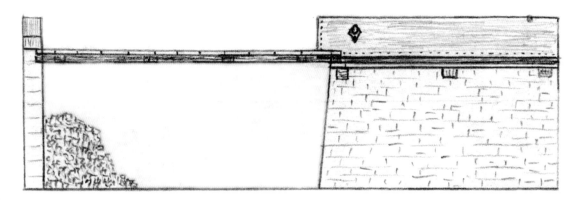

26 Caboosh

Having got some idea of the approximate size of a lump pan maybe it should be explained how a larger pan could be made shorter. In some lump yards, pans could be found that were longer than was required for lumping. Therefore they could be used either as common pans or lump pans.

A pan could be made shorter by putting a plate across (27). This could be made of light plate bolted together and bolted to the inside of the pan. When this was put into a pan it could be used as a lump pan at the front end, and while it was used as a lump pan the salt that was made at the back side of the plate, when it was drawn out, could be used for common salt. When a plate was put into a pan like this, it would be said that it had a mid-feather in it.

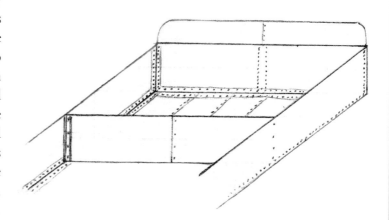

27 Lump pan made shorter

Having got some idea what the lump pan looked like, let us look at the common or fishery pan. These were built the same way as the lump pan only longer in length. They did not have any dogs on the inside as no tubs were used round these pans. They had hurdles on each side of the pan like the lump pan but the salt from these pans was put into a warehouse where it would drain and dry until wanted.

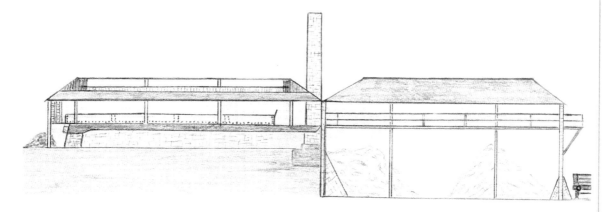

28 The arrangement of common or fishery pans

Sketch 28 shows how the common or fishery pans were set out. It shows the pan and the warehouse behind it. It will be noticed that a staging near the top of the warehouse runs on a level with the pan. This made it possible for the wallers (the men who used to empty these pans) to run the salt from the hurdle straight into the warehouse and then be able to tip it where it was wanted. However, it should be pointed out that the size and depth of the warehouses varied according to where they were built. Some would be seven or eight feet deep (2.5m) others could be twenty feet deep (6m).

Having looked at the layout of the common and fishery pan and the warehouse, next it can be shown how the stages running into the warehouses were erected if the works were built on the steep bank of a river and the pans were at the top of the bank and the warehouse at the bottom.

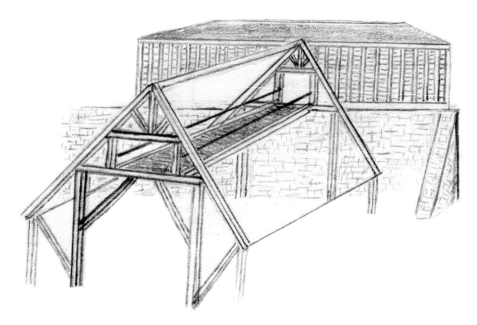

29 Staging used in warehouse

Sketch 29 shows just a straight part of the type of staging used in the warehouse, but it would be noticed on most saltworks that the staging would have branches running from it into other warehouses.

In this type of warehouse the floors were always made of common brick. The reason being that besides being a floor, it was also one great big drain. It should be understood that after this type of salt had been taken from the pan it would first be put onto the hurdle on each side of the pan and while it was on the hurdle a lot of the brine that was in it would drain away through the space that was between the hurdle planks. However, even after it had been taken from the hurdles and put into the warehouse, it would still contain a considerable amount of brine.

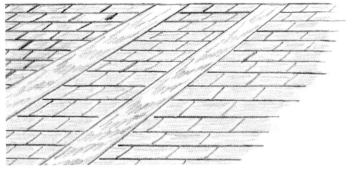

30 Bricks and planks on the warehouse floor

If one looked at the bricks in a warehouse floor, it would be noticed that they were not laid tightly together but were laid slightly apart. It would also be noticed that no mortar was used, instead they were laid on fine cinders. Planks were laid so they were lying 'spaced out' in the floor. These planks were laid to cover the drains. So it will be understood that the bricks laid on the cinders would allow the to drain through and then into the drains (30).

It must not be forgotten that there was another way of building walls and this method used the clinkers that were taken from the pan fires when they were being cleaned. The clinkers were called bass, and built with black mortar, made a very strong wall. Black mortar was used in the buildings about the salt works both with brick and bass and was made on the works. It was made of cinders and lime and although called black mortar, was a very dark grey in colour. It was not difficult to get any amount of black mortar because all salt works had their own lime pit which was lump lime slaked down and used round the salt pans and also for whitewashing the inside of the different buildings. Most salt works also had their own mortar mill. So, with plenty of cinders from the pan fires, lime and a mortar mill, making black mortar was no problem.

Sketch 31 will give some idea what a bass wall looked like with its rough surface. This has two openings which would have been used for windows.

There was another type of mortar used. This was salt mortar which was made with a mixture of lime and salt. This

31 Bass Wall

was used in the hothouses on the top of the flues and also on the hothouse floors. This kind of mortar was never used outside as it would not stand up to the weather. It was only useful where it could be kept dry and warm and in these conditions would keep quite hard and strong.

Another thing that should be explained is the number of fires that were under a pan. It has been shown that some pans had four fires. It should also be pointed out that some of them also had three fires under them. It might be of some interest to see how those fires were built up.

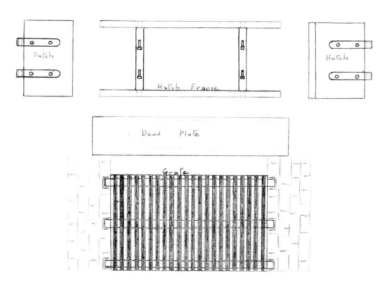

32 fire grates

Sketch 32 shows how the fire grates were made up. The brick pillars were called the solids. The dead plate was a thick metal plate which was placed across from one solid to another. At the back of this two or three steel rails were fastened across. These were put to support the grate bars which were laid on and not fastened. At the front the hatch frame was put up and the front bricked up. When completed this was called the forby. The strip on the hatch covers the centre when closed.

In earlier sketches it has been shown that there was a chimney to each pan. However, if one had gone onto some works it would have been found that more than one pan went into one chimney. If one had gone onto Seddon's works at Brooks Lane, Middlewich, which was a small works with four lump pans and three common pans, you would have seen that two lump pans went into one chimney, that three common pans went into another chimney, but that the other two lump pans each had a separate chimney.

So here again going from one works to another you would find that the roofs would look a bit different as was the use of the chimneys.

2 The Salt Makers, Lumpmen

The lumpman not only made the salt in the pan he worked but also made the salt into lumps. It may be asked, did it take a big man to do this job? Of course it did not make any difference. There were big built men who did the job but there were also men under five feet six (1.67m) who also did this job from when they were young men till they were old.

33 Lumpman

Before the lumpman's work is looked at the clothes that he wore should be explained. The shirt was a loose fitting garment with no collar and short sleeves reaching to just below the elbow. He also wore a pair of loose fitting trousers called drawers by the saltworkers (34). Maybe they got this name from the tapes that were always put on the sides of the trouser legs at the bottom, making it possible to fasten the bottoms of the trousers round about the legs if wanted. Of course the men working round the pans or in the hothouses never fastened them because they wanted their clothing as loose as possible.

34 Drawers

35 Body belt

It will be noticed that the legs of these drawers came to just below the knee. It should be also explained that the working clothes were always made of grey or dark blue flannel. The lumpman's long stockings reached to just below the knee.

He also wore clogs. These were leather topped, with wooden soles. They had metal tips on the bottom of the soles and a small brass toe-cap. Around the tops of the clogs and his ankle, the lumpman used to wrap pieces of cloth. These were called buzzgins and were worn to stop any salt or brine or bits of coal from going into his clogs.

Some of the old lumpmen used to wear a kind of body belt (35). These were made of red or blue flannel and were fastened at the front by tapes. The reason they were worn was to protect the bottom of the back from getting cold or getting a chill and they proved to be very effective, for during cold weather there were quite a number of cold draughts round a lump pan. It should be pointed out that in days gone by the lumpman had to buy all his own flannels and clogs.

The lumpman's job used to start from very early on a Monday morning 'till Saturday noon. So, starting on a Monday morning between three and four o'clock for a twelve hour shift pan then two men would start to work. However, if it was an eight hour shift pan then three men would start.

The first job would be to take the salt out of the pan. This would be common salt, that is salt that would have been made over the week-end while the pan was cooling off after the weeks work. It should be understood that after the pan had finished lumping it would still have quite a lot of heat in it and this is what would continue to make salt while the pan was dropping back over the week-end, as it was called.

The method used to get the salt from the pan was for the men to stand on each side of the pan and use a raker to pull the salt to the side of the pan. Then they would lift the salt out with a skimmer and pile it onto the hurdle. This was called drawing the pan.

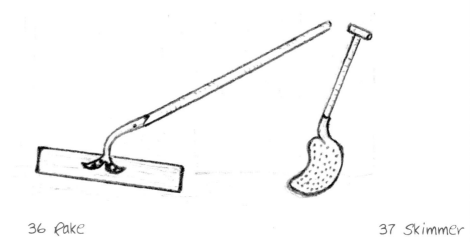

36 Rake   37 Skimmer

The raker blade (36) was a piece of steel plate about two feet six inches long about seven inches wide and an eighth of an inch thick (760mm x 180mm x 3mm). This would have a stail fitted to it which was about ten feet long (3m). The skimmer (37) was like a round steel shovel with holes in it and this was used to lift the salt out of the pan, the holes allowing the brine to run away as the salt was lifted out.

After the salt had been drawn from the pan, the cotter patches would be taken off. These were covering the holes at the back end of the pan. Of course, this would allow the brine to run away and empty the pan. While the pan was emptying the common salt would be loaded into box barrows or salt carts and then taken and tipped into the warehouse where the bulk salt was stored. This was called 'whare-rusing' the salt. So this is how two names were used to describe one place. If a man was taking salt to the warehouse and tipping it in this was called 'whare-rusing'. However, if a man or men were working in the warehouse it would be said that they were working in the 'store-rus'.

The box barrow (38) was quite a big barrow, the length of the main frame being about four feet nine inches (1.4m) to the end of the handles, the width at the top being two feet wide (0.6m). So it can be understood that this type of barrow would carry quite a good weight of salt.

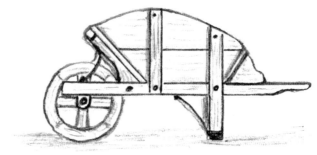

38 Box Barrow

After the lumpmen had removed the salt from the hurdles they would then start to clean the pan out because, by then, the brine would have emptied out of the pan. First of all they would get the salt from the sides of the pan. This was done by going round the outside of the pan and giving the side plate a smack with a hammer. This would cause the salt on the inside to fall away and drop onto the bottom of the pan and break up into pieces. These were called seggurs. This was the salt that had accumulated on the inside of the pan during the week and during the week-end. The seggurs would then be thrown out of the pan onto the hurdle. With some firms this salt would be taken away and used as soiled salt, with others it would be thrown away as waste salt or put under the hurdles. During the weeks lumping the water that was used to wash the tubs out and wash the hurdles down would drop through the hurdles and wash the waste salt away.

After the seggurs had been thrown out the lumpmen would wash the pan down with buckets of water. This was done to wash any salt away that was lying on the scale on the bottom of the pan. The reason being that the salt scale had to be broken up with hammers and if any salt was left on it, this would splash all over the men and if any of it splashed into their eyes it was very painful.

After being washed off, the scale on the bottom of the pan would be broken up with hammers and thrown out of the pan (39). Again, this scale would be ground up and used as soiled salt by some firms, by others thrown away as waste. After all of the scale had been thrown out, the pan would then be well washed out with water. When this had been done the inside of the side of the pan might be white-washed. The sides of the pan were called the rim of the pan and if white-washing them this would be called white-washing the rim plate of the pan.

Now the lumpmen had got the pan clean the cotter patches at the back of the pan would be put on and fastened down with the cotter pin. After this had been done fresh brine would be run into the pan.

39 Picking the lump pan on Monday morning

It should be said that the scale on a hand-it pan as a rule was quite a lot thicker than it was on a Lagos pan. Sketch 39 shows what it would be like early on a Monday morning when a lump pan was being picked. It shows one man breaking the scale up with a hammer while the other man is prising the scale from the bottom of the pan with a crowbar.

After the job of drawing and picking the pan had been done and the brine was running into the pan, the man on the morning shift would then start putting the fires under the pan. This was called gateing the pan. The rest of the men would then go home, to come back on later shifts. If it was a twelve hour pan the shifts would be worked from four o'clock in the morning until four in the afternoon, and the night man from four in the afternoon until four the following morning. An eight hour shift pan would be worked from four in the morning until twelve noon, then twelve noon till eight in the evening and then eight till four o'clock the following morning. This would carry on for one week then the men would change shifts which would mean that the night man would go on to the morning shift.

40 Working in the holes stoking the pan

The holes were where the lumpman worked when he was firing the pan. Figure 40 shows the hatchways through which the coal was thrown to feed the fires and each of them had two metal doors. It also shows the raker, the slicer, the hook and the ranger which would be used when the lumpman was cleaning the fires, such as getting out the clinkers or bass or any other dead cinders which would be stopping the fires from burning as they should do.

After the morning shiftman had put the fires under the pan, he would then wash the hurdles down with buckets of water. After doing this he would then start to wash the salt tubs out and set them out on the hurdles, two rows on each hurdle. This was called ranking the tubs. The number of tubs to be worked would be decided by the lumpman himself, possibly between twenty-five to thirty in each row. While the pan was starting to get hot it would start to make a small amount of salt and after a few hours the lumpman would take this out. He would start at the front of the pans over the fires and he would rake this salt to the back end of the pan, first doing one side of the pan and then doing the other side. When he had done this and raked it to each side of the pan at the back end, he would then lift the salt out with his skimmer and put it on the hurdle. This job was done so as to make sure that the pan was clean and fit to start lumping. This was called raking the pan down, and this was done to all the lump pans. The amount of salt taken out on this occasion was not a lot, possibly a salt cart full and this was taken to the warehouse.

Of course it should be pointed out that in between these various jobs the lumpman would keep going down to look at his fires to see that these were burning up. He would want his pan to make salt as soon as possible because if he was not making lumps he would not be making any money. Sometime after raking the pan down the lumpman would look at the pan and if he decided there was enough salt in it he would start tubbing it.

Before going on with the lumpman's job the types of salt which were generally made in the lump pans should be explained. First of all there were the light shoots which were called Lagos salt, then there were the heavy shoots which were called hand-it lumps. There have been various tales told that different lumpmen used to use various things in the pan so that it would make the salt better, but none seemed to be very reliable. However, two things used were soft soap and glue. If the pan was making light shoots called Lagos, sometime during his shift when he thought it necessary the lumpman would take a piece of glue about three inches long by half inch wide (76mm x 12mm) and the thickness of the glue which was quite thin. He would throw this into the pan at the back of the part where it was boiling.

If the pan was making heavy shoots, called hand-its, he would take a handful of salt from the top of a tub, dip his fingers into the soft soap box, and then mix the soft soap and salt together until it was crumbly then throw this across the back of the boil. These were the two things used for making lump pan salt, glue for making the Lagos salt and soft soap for making the hand-it salt. This was what was called doping the pan.

When the lumpmen decided that there was enough salt in the pan to start tubbing it, he would first have to rake it to the side of a pan, so he would begin by raking it clear from over the fires at the front end of the pan and then continue down one side of the pan till he got to the back end, raking it close to the side as he went along. The lumpman had two rakers on each side of the pan, a long one to reach the middle of the pan and a short one to pull the salt close to the side of the pan (41).

41 Lumpman raking salt

What he raked up would fill one row of tubs, and after he had done that he would have to rake the salt up again before he could fill another row. After he had raked his salt up he would then start to fill the tubs. He would start by lifting the first tub into the dogs, this is the metal shelf that is hanging just inside the rimplate of the pan. When he had filled his first row he would then go to the other side of the pan, rake the salt to the side and then fill a row of tubs on that side. When he had done that he would then come back to the side on which he started.

He would then take the first row he had filled off the dogs and put them onto the hurdle. He would then rake his salt up and start to fill another row. When he had done this he would then go back to the other side and fill another row there. When he had got four rows filled he would then rake off any salt that might have fallen onto the bottom of the pan over the fires. After he had done this he would then go down to the holes to see if his fires were alright. After he had attended to the fires, he would come back and start to empty the first row of tubs that he had filled. This was called turning a row out. If he was making Lagos salt he would turn half the row out and then get his happer and give each lump a few pats round the top to straighten any rough salt that was on it. Then he would empty the rest of the row and do the same with those. When he had turned them all out he would get his barrow, load it with lumps and wheel them into the hothouse where he would put them into one of the ditches. When he had finished putting the first row into the hothouse he would then get his bucket, fill it with water, wash the salt off his barrow and then wash all the emptied tubs out. If he did not do this, any salt that had been left in could spoil his lumps when he filled his tubs with salt again.

During his week's work a lumpman used a great amount of water. Every time he turned a row of lumps out he had to wash the tubs and the hurdle. He also had to keep his raker and skimmer washed because if he let them get encrusted with salt he would very soon get sore fingers and hands. Having got his first row into the hothouse and the tubs washed up, he would then take the tubs that were on the dogs and put these onto the hurdle. He would then rake the salt to the side of the pan and start to fill the tubs that he had emptied. When he had filled this row he would then go to the other side of the pan and do the same thing there.

Well, that was the Lagos lumpman's job. Firing the pan so that it would make salt, keeping the salt from dropping onto the pan plate over the fires and filling and emptying the tubs and running the lumps into the hothouse.

The hand-it lumpman's job was just the same, the difference being that the hand-it lumpman made heavier salt and he also had to happ the lumps better than the Lagos lumpman. The reason for this was that Lagos lumps were made, put through a grinding mill and then put into bags, but a hand-it lump was sold in the lump. Therefore, there was a bit more work put into the finishing of the hand-it lump and some lumpmen used to be proud of the way they could happ a lump. A hand-it lumpman never turned more than two or three lumps out onto the hurdle at one time. If he did, he would not be able to happ them properly because the brine would have drained out of the top of the lump and leave it too dry for happing. So the hand-it man turned two or three lumps out and then happed them while they are soft at the top, and when he had finished happing them they would look very straight and clean with square corners. You did not have to look to see if a lump was being happed, because you could hear the smack and slap of the happer from quite a number of yards away. There have been occasions when after a man had happed a hand-it lump he would put his happer on the top of the lump and then stand on it. This was considered a very clever thing to do and a man had to be a good happer of lumps to be able to do this.

So that is the difference between a hand-it and a Lagos lumpman. Of course the hand-it man got slightly more pay for his job.

 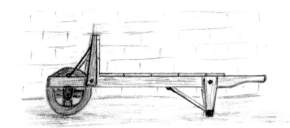

42 Lump happer   43 Lump barrow

The lump happer (42) looks like a wooden bat. It is about twelve inches long (300mm) which includes the handle and blade and about six inches wide and it is about three eighths of an inch thick tapering off to one eighth (150mm x 9mm x 3mm). The lump barrow (43) is a flat barrow which the lumpman used to take the lumps into the hothouse. When the lumpman loaded the lumps onto this barrow he had to put one lump over one of the legs at the back first, if he did not do this and put one at the front the barrow would topple over.

44 Lumpman filling the tubs with salt

It should be explained that when the lumpmen were working round the pan there was always a great amount of steam and more often than not it was impossible to see across the pan. Sketch 44 shows the lumpman wearing a flannel shirt but very often he would be working stripped to the waist. A lot of the old lumpmen used to go and collect thin round reeds out of the fields near their homes and put them into their clogs.

45 Skimmer held by lumpman   46 Skimmer held by waller

The lumpman and the waller held their skimmer differently. A lumpman would hold his skimmer with his left hand underneath the ein which allowed him to get plenty of lift so that he could get the skimmer full of salt to the height of the tub (45). A waller did not have to lift his skimmer full of salt as high as the lumpman. What he had to do was to lift it over the rim of the pan and drop the salt onto the hurdle (46). The two sketches show how a right handed man would hold the skimmer, the left hand doing the lifting.

We can show how some lumpmen had the kosp on their skimmer set. On a shovel or spade the kosp is set in a line with the blade but some lumpmen had the kosp on a skimmer set at an angle, this gave a slight leverage when the skimmer was turned to empty the salt into the tub and it also saved the lumpman from turning his wrist over too far.

47 Kosp set straight

48 Kosp set at an angle

The kosp in Sketch 47 is set straight and the kosp in Sketch 48 is set at an angle, and this is how some lumpmen had them set. The one set at an angle would be for the use of a right handed man.

Filling the tubs was tubbing. It should be pointed out that doing this, plus the evaporation of the brine, gradually lowers the level of the brine in the pan. The lumpman stops the brine from getting too low by setting the two valves at the front of the pan which control the brine feed to the pan (49).

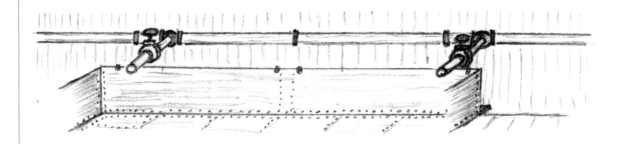

49 How brine is let into a lump pan

The brine that is let into the lump pan comes along a main pipe from the brine tank or cistern.

One of the things a lumpman did not like was brine dropping onto the bottom of the pan over the fires. The reason for this was that if the salt dropped and formed scale the lumpman had to get his dodging hammer, break the scale loose and then take it out and he did not get any payment for doing this. If the scale was left on it could cause the pan to blow. This would blow scale and hot brine up into the air and if anyone was nearby it could be quite dangerous. Another thing that could happen, if scale blew, was that the salt in the pan would go discoloured which made it no good for making lumps because the salt would have a brown colour. So it can be seen why the lumpman would never let any salt get fast over the fires if he could help it. That is why he would see that his fires were kept well raked off. Some lumpmen could tell if scale was fast on the fire by the smell, this was a smell of burnt pudding. If they caught a smell of that they soon took steps to remove it. It was said of a lumpman that he was a man who when he dropped one tool had to pick another up. Of course the reason was that if he did not do this then he did not make any money.

50 Lumpman happing a lump

Sketch 50 shows the lumpman happing a lump after he has turned them out of the tub. It also shows the barrow that he would use to wheel the lumps into the hothouse.

There were a different number of lumps that were made by the lumpman. First of all there would be the Lagos lump, these were a fairly large lump and were called seventy-two's, which means that seventy-two of these lumps had to be made to count as a ton (1,016kg). There were also a very small number of light lumps made which were called nineties, they were given this name because they were made in a smaller tub and therefore ninety had to be made to count as a ton. These were sometimes made at Seddon's Brooks Lane Works at Middlewich, but Lagos lumps were mainly made in the larger tubs. The hand-it lumps were the heavier lumps and these were made in different sizes. First there were the eighties, which were eighty to the ton, then there were the hundreds and the hundred and twenties. The eighties and the hundred and twenties were sold in the block as they were. Some salt firms who purchased the eighties then sawed them up into smaller blocks to be sold in the shops. The hundreds were classed as works lumps and were used for sawing up into smaller blocks. These hundreds were sometimes made at Seddon's Brooks Lane Works at Middlewich.

The salt tubs were made of elm and fastened with brass nails.

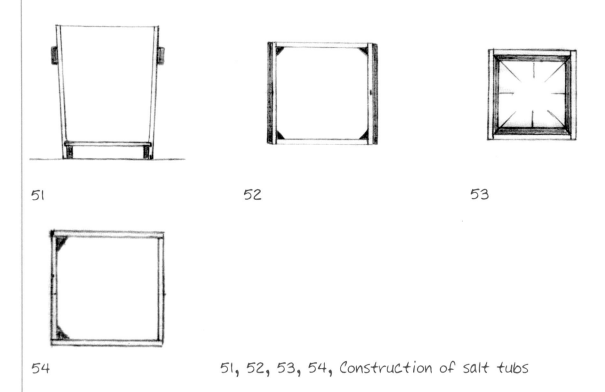

51

52

53

54
51, 52, 53, 54, Construction of salt tubs

This type of tub would be used to make a seventy-two lump. The sides of the tub had blocks of wood that are fastened on to provide a means of lifting the tubs about (51). The bottom of the tub is rebated into the sides and then blocks put under to give extra strength to the bottom of the tub, and also the bottom is kept clear of the floor.

Sketch 52 shows the top of the tub. The shaded part on each side being the lifting handles. Also the corners on the inside are shaded. These are strips that are nailed into the corners going the length of the tub inside, which makes the lumps slide out of the tub more easily.

Sketch 53 shows the bottom of the tub, the shaded parts being the blocks that are put under the bottom. The lines that are going from the outside to the centre are saw cuts that are put into the bottom of the tub so as to allow the brine to drain away which gets put into the tub with the salt.

All the tubs are made the same, the difference being in the size. However, in an eighty tub (54) there were only two strips inside the tub. This was because the lump could be used for sawing up into smaller blocks and if there were four strips this would have caused waste on each side of the lumps. Of course it was a bit more difficult to turn a lump out with only two strips in the tub and very often the lumpman would have to rock the tub backwards and forwards and sideways to get the lump to leave the tub. So it can be understood that turning the tubs over and then lifting them up off the lumps was a very back-aching job.

55 Wheeling the lumps into the hothouse

To watch a lumpman pulling one of those barrows behind him loaded with lumps looked an easy thing to do (55). If the lumpman had eight hand-its on his barrow such as eight eighties he would be pulling about two hundredweight (109kg). Also those barrows wanted quite a bit of balancing and if they went over a little too much to one side then a lump or two might fall off and if that happened then it was the lumpman's loss for he didn't get paid for broken lumps.

It may be of some interest to see how the weight and count of the lumps was kept. First of all the different size tubs were made to take the salt. As the lumpman made the lumps and took them into the hothouses he kept a count of them himself but the firm also kept count by employing a man to count them as well. He was called a lump counter. His job was to count the number of lumps in each ditch after it was filled up. This count was then used to check against the lumpman's count. The weight of the lumps was more particular on the hand-it lump than the Lagos lump.

Every so often, without telling the lumpman when it was going to be done, the foreman would come to the hothouse with a couple of men and a set of scales. The men would then take four or five lumps at random off a flue. These would be weighed and the average weight taken. Possibly this would be done on all the flues in the hothouse and if lumps were found to be light then the lumpman got a good ticking off. However it was very rare that a hand-it lumpman had his lumps underweight and of course Lagos lumps had to be light. At one time, to get a solid lump, a lumpman used to have to mundle each tub, which meant that when he had filled the tub with salt he then had to get a short shaft and podge this up and down inside the tub to get the salt as solid as possible and for doing this he got paid a few coppers extra. However in later years this was done away with.

Of course if one watched a lumpman filling his tubs when he put the last skimmerfull in, he would give the tub a tap with his skimmer then drop it onto the salt on the top of the tub before pushing the excess salt off the top and doing this would help to get a solid lump.

It used to be said that the art of lumping was having good fires under the pan and this was true because on odd occasions when a pan had been neglected and not kept hot enough the salt would be no use for tubbing. Some lumpmen would say that it had gone rotten. It could be put into the tubs but when it came to be turned out, instead of a lump standing there when the tub was lifted up all that there would be would be a small pile of salt and that would not be much use for anything except to put into the warehouse.

56 Chipping paddle

At the finish of his shift the lumpman used a chipping paddle. To clear the salt that had fastened to the rim of the pan on the inside. Some had a wooden stand and metal blade. Some were all metal and had a six inch (150mm) blade.

What has not been mentioned is where the lumpman had his meals. Well, in days gone by there were no canteens on any open pan salt works. So not only the lumpman but all the other workers had to take their own meals with them.

If he wanted a couple of eggs for his meal he could put these into the pan where they would float on the top of the brine and cook.

When a lumpman found time to have a meal he would quite often go and sit in the hothouse where there would be some sort of seat such as a plank laid on bricks. If there wasn't one then he would very possibly sit on the end of the flues. If it was too hot in the hothouse then he might sit at the backend of the pan.

One of the things he always had was a big can of tea which he carried from home. This he would use all through his shift, very often drinking part of it and then filling it up with cold water and if he wanted it hot he would possibly put it into the pan to heat it up. It should be understood that the lumpman drank quite an amount of tea during his shift.

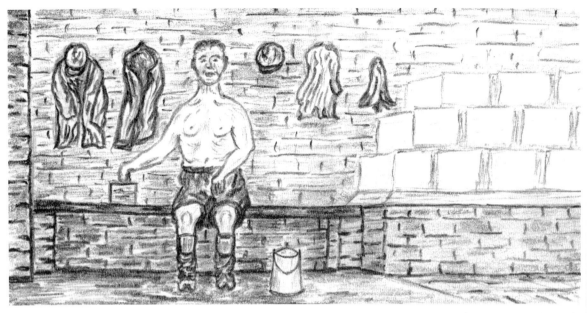

57 Lumpman having a meal break

When having his meal in the hothouse his can was never far away from him (57). His clothes were hung on the nails in the wall. This is where he used to change his clothes before starting work. The hothouse was also the place where he used to hang his flannels to dry after his shift when he had washed them out in fresh water. There's no doubt the lumpman had a rough, tough job.

If he wanted a wash, a short while before the end of his shift he would fill a bucket with cold water and then place it in the pan so that it would be hot for when he wanted it.

It could be asked why did men have this kind of work. Some of the old lumpmen would say "Well, I used to go into the works when I was a lad and help my father to turn a few rows out, or help him to run some lumps into the hothouse, or wash the tubs and hurdles up." And this they would say is how they became lumpmen. Others would say that they had a family to keep and lumpmen's money was more than general labouring. And then some would say that when they started lumping there were no other jobs to be had. Then, of course, in days gone by it was the lumpman's wife who would often go and help him with his work.

So tales of how a man became a lumpman were very varied. It makes one wonder how the lumpman used to manage to do their work years ago when there was no decent lighting and when there were only tallow candles or duck lamps. The conditions were bad enough when there was electric lighting and the steam was making it impossible to see the length or the width of a pan, so the conditions that the lumpmen worked in during the early open pan days must have been terrible.

58 Duck lamp

A duck lamp was filled with oil and would be stood on an upturned salt tub. The light from it was not very good and it also gave off a very dirty smoke from the wick which was coiled up inside with the end going out through the spout. So it can be imagined the very poor conditions that the old lumpmen worked in years ago.

After looking at the lumpman's job the way he was paid should be explained. When drawing common salt he was paid for the amount that was taken into the salt warehouse. It has been said earlier that he took this to the warehouse by a barrow or a salt cart.

It may be asked, how did they know how much these barrows or carts carried ?

Well, a simple method was used. The barrow or cart was filled with salt. This was then tipped out and the salt was put into hundred weight (51kg) bags and weighed on a set of scales. When it had been found how much weight they carried then it would be said so many barrows or carts to the ton (1,016kg). Of course this varied because if it was light salt there would be more carts or barrows to the ton than there would be with heavy salt. So when the lumpmen took their salt to the warehouse a tally would be kept on the number of carts or barrows and they would be paid for the tons that they put in.

Next he would be paid for picking of the pan. This was not paid on how many tons of scale they threw out, but was paid at a fixed rate for breaking the scale up, throwing it out of the pan and washing the pan out.

The gateing and heating of the pan was also paid for at a rate for the job. The other payment was for the tons of lumps that they put into the hothouses which varied from forty odd to fifty tons (40,600kg-50,800kg).

The common pan picking and gateing had to be divided between the number of men working the pan but as a rule it would be found that the lumpmen also divided the payment for the lumps between each other because they worked as a team around the pans.

The firing and cleaning or bassing of the fires was another job that had to be done. If it was a pan with four fires and had three men working it some would work it so that the morning man bassed two fires and the night man bassed two fires. This left the afternoon man with none to bass. Instead he would put some extra rows of lumps into the hothouse. However, if only two men worked the pan on twelve hours then they would have two fires each to bass. If it was a three fired pan and two men worked it then the day man would possibly bass two fires and the night man one. So this gives some idea of how the lumpmen used to look after the firing of the pans which was very important.

If an open pan was looked at when it was making salt it would have been noticed that when the salt was making it would look like a very thin skin on the surface of the brine. And this would keep breaking away in flakes and sink to the bottom of the pan. When this was happening it would be said that the pan had a nice set on it. Another remark that would be made if a lump pan was making salt nicely and small bubbles were coming to the surface and going "plip plop, plip plop" it would be said that she was doing a bit of chuckling.

In a hand-it pan in which soft soap was used for doping, if the lumpman over doped it, which he rarely did, having too much soap in the pan would cause a tight skin, like the skin on a pudding, to form over the surface of the brine and this would stop the pan from making because the skin would form so tight it would not break away and fall to the bottom of the pan. When this happened the lumpman would have to keep breaking the skin up by flicking brine across it with his skimmer or happer till it started to fall again.

There are one or two other things that were said to have been used by different lumpmen such as putting bits of butter or a bit of tobacco, or a few flakes of shellac in. One chap was said to have put a cow heel in his pan on one occasion. Of course these were tales that were told by some of the lumpmen. If they were true or not it is difficult to say.

If a pan got a leak in the plate in the bottom of the pan while it was working, it would be said that the pan was running. Very often this could be stopped by putting some thick stodgy lime over the place where the brine was leaking through. Of course if it was a bad leak such as a plate that had split over the fires then sometimes a "bag" put over it with thick lime would stop it and the pan would carry on making till the end of the week. However, if so much brine was running out that it was putting a fire out then the word would go round the lumpyard that such and such a pan had calved.

Another thing should be looked at that had one or two different names. This was the water butt which was very important to the lumpman because without plenty of water the lumpman's job was made more difficult, and there have been plenty of heated arguments between lumpmen and the works foreman when there has not been enough water running into the butts which from lumpman to lumpman would get a different name such as the tub, the boss or the bosh. It may be asked where did all the water come from. It was just where the works were built. If they were built near to a canal then canal water would be used or if the works were built near a river then river water would have been used.

Before leaving the lump pans let us look at another way that was used to make Lagos salt. This was made in the open pan but no tubs were used, instead it was made in bulk. This way of making Lagos was done at Seddon's Brooks Lane Works, Middlewich. The method was thought out by a man who worked as a waller there named Bill Kettle and it was done in the pans that had been used for making common salt. First of all the pans were cut back to make them shorter.

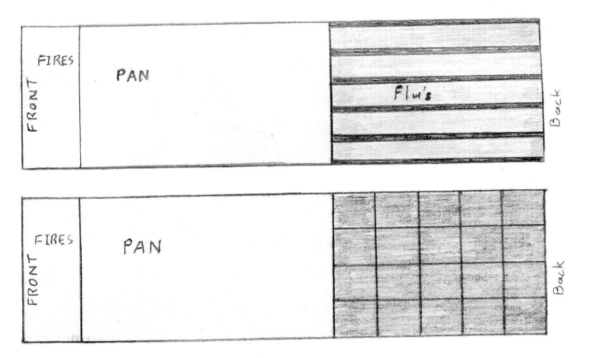

59 Pan cut back

60 Plates covered with thick layer of mortar

When the pan was cut back it exposed the flues at the back end (59). These were covered with metal plates and the plates were then covered with a thick layer of salt mortar (60). So here was a pan making Lagos salt which had a hot plate at the backend for drying it. The salt was drawn out of the pan and put onto the hurdle to drain. While it was draining the salt that had dried on the hot plate was run into the warehouse. Then the salt was taken from the hurdle and put onto the hot plate for drying.

The salt that was in the warehouse was put through a grinding mill when it was required and bagged and exported to Africa. These pans had two firemen working twelve hour shifts seven days a week and they were picked and cleaned out after they had been worked a certain number of weeks. The pans were drawn by the wallers working one on each side of the pan and they worked seven days a week from four in the morning till about eleven o'clock. This job was not paid on tonnage but at a given rate for the job. The conditions on this job were very warm as the pans were drawn while they were hot, the same as a lump pan. Also, when they were working on the hot plate it was very hot to the feet. However it was never considered to be as good as the salt made by the lumpman with the tubs and the tonnage turned out was not as good.

Of course this and other things were tried to keep the open pan production up. At ICI at Winsford they tried to get the lumpmen to work on a seven shift base but this didn't work. At this firm they stopped picking the pans every week, instead they were dodged by the lumpman to clear the fires of scale and carried on lumping, only picking after working a number of weeks. Other things were tried such as having fibre-glass salt tubs which were much lighter to lift about, but these were never as good as the wooden salt tubs. Also different types of lighter tools were tried.

A lumpman's tools only seemed to become handy when they were almost worn out such as a skimmer when it had worn thin and some lumpmen would keep one as long as possible. If anyone used it or took it there was liable to be a noise about it. Another thing was the happer which seemed to become handier as it got worn down. One of the things that some lumpmen or wallers would do was to get a skimmer out of the store room and then hide it away under the hurdle or some other place so that it would rust away and get a bit lighter by the time that he wanted to use it. This was also done by some of the labourers with shovels. A trick that was done with a new shovel was to stick the top of the ein and kosp into the fire under one of the pans then burn it down so much. When it was pulled out, the charred wood would be scraped off which would then make the ein and kosp thinner and much handier to use.

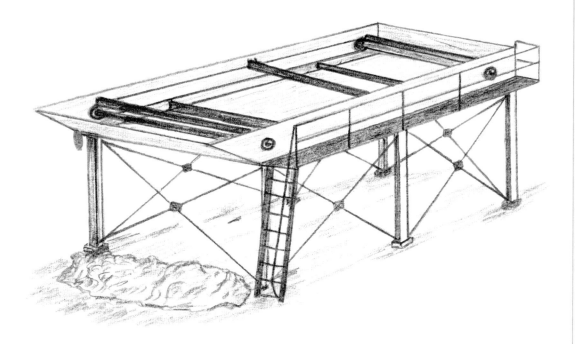

61 Experimental pan at the Vacuum Plant, Winsford

An experimental pan was tried at the vacuum plant at Winsford (61). This was only a small open pan. It was built above ground level and at one end was built like a ramp. It was steam heated and it had a continuous belt in it. On this belt were fastened scrapers which stretched across the width of the pan. As the salt was made and fell to the bottom of the pan, the scraper pushed it along to the edge of the ramp where the salt fell over the edge of the pan to the floor below from where it was moved away. What was learned from this is difficult to say.

One thing that has not been mentioned and which might be of interest is the amount of brine that was used to make a ton (1,016kg) of open pan salt. Of course there was a certain amount of brine wasted in the process when they emptied the pans after drawing down the week-end common salt. Of course it had to be done so that the pans could be picked and cleaned out. Then as the lumps were made and taken from the pan there was a certain amount of drainage, both on the hurdle and after they had been put into the hothouse.

At Winsford Salt Works the lump pans in later years were not emptied every week so there was a saving of brine as well as time. Another method that was tried was to pump the brine from one pan that was needed cleaning to another that was clean. However, at Middlewich, the pans were emptied and picked every week up to the end of the production of open pan salt. At Murgatroyd's a weekly check was kept on the gallons of brine that went through the meter to the open pan works. When it was put against the tons of salt made on the works it worked out at one thousand gallons of brine to every ton of salt produced (4,546 litres to 1,016 kg), one ton of coal to two tons of salt (1,016kg to 2,032kg).

3 The Salt Makers, Wallers

The wallers were another hard working group of salt workers who like the lumpmen and lofters worked hard for the money they got. It can be understood how the lumpmen got their name by making lumps, also the lofters who had to throw lumps through the traps into the room or the loft above the hothouses but it's difficult to say how the wallers got their name.

It could have been from the fact that when the wallers had finished drawing a pan the salt lay on the hurdles from one end to the other forming a complete wall of salt.

The pans that the waller emptied were longer than the lump pans and the waller's job was to take the salt from these pans and put it onto the hurdle where it would drain. After this he would load the salt into the carts and take it and tip it into the warehouse. The types of salt made in these bigger pans had different names. There was the common salt, the light Boston common salt, the butter salt and the fishery salt.

The common pans were as a rule drawn by two men. One man worked on each side of the pan and if two pans were working together one would be drawn every other day. Then there was a coarse heavy salt with a larger grain than the common salt. This of course took longer to make than the common salt. Some would be ten-day fishery and some would be a month to six weeks. When these pans were being drawn there would be at least six wallers, three on one side and three on the other - one man on each side at the back end of the pan, one on each side in the middle and one on each side at the front end. It would be found that there was not a lot of salt at the front end over the fires and when this was drawn out it would have quite a lot of bits of scale in it. This would be put on the hurdle in a pile and not mixed with the other salt.

This salt would later be put through a riddle by a couple of labourers to get the scale out of it (62).

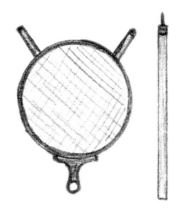

62 Riddling salt to remove scale

63 Riddle and leg

The labourers used a riddle with two handles on it on one side, on the other side was a plate from which a piece of metal with an eye in it extended. This was then placed on the top of a wooden leg which had a metal peg at the top. It was then pushed backwards and forwards to riddle the salt (63).

After the wallers at the front of the pan had cleared the fires they would then work their way back along the pan till they joined up with the others at the back end where they would all work until the pan was empty.

Of course it was not always straight forward getting the salt out of the fishery pan. Sometimes it would have set quite hard on the bottom of the pan. When this happened it made the job much harder. Sometimes it could be broken up by lifting the raker up in the air and then bringing it hard down onto the salt. Or they would get a chipping paddle with a stail in it about ten feet long which they would push under the salt and try to loosen it that way.

If it couldn't be loosened by these methods, then there have been times when they have had to take their clogs and stockings off, roll up the legs of their drawers, get into the pan and break it up with a shovel. It might be asked "Why didn't they let all the brine out of the pan and then shovel it out ?" Well of course, it was easier to get the salt out by raking it to the side with the raker and lifting it out with skimmer. Also, the salt was very much cleaner when it was lifted out with plenty of brine in the pan.

To get back to how the wallers worked. After they had drawn the pan they would usually go for their breakfast. What has not been said is that the wallers like the lumpmen used to turn out early in the morning to do their job but unlike the lumpmen the wallers used to have a place of their own in which to have their meals. This was called the wallers hut (64).

64 Inside the wallers' hut

In the wallers' hut they changed their clothes, dried their work clothes after finishing work and had their meals. There were wooden forms round the hut and the coal stove was kept burning night and day. They dried their clothing by hanging them on lines which stretched across the hut.

After the wallers had had their breakfast they would then get the salt carts ready for loading with salt. The salt carts were used to run the salt into the warehouse. This was called whare-rusing the salt. They would move the salt off both hurdles at once. If there were six wallers there would be three on each hurdle. One man would run the full cart to the warehouse while the other two filled one (65).

65 Waller carting salt to warehouse

These men were paid for the number of tons they put into the warehouse, so each salt cart was counted as it went in. With some salt it would run out at around three carts to the ton and the chap who was doing the counting would keep his eyes on the carts to see that they were all full up.

It should be explained that years ago the wheels of those salt carts had flat metal tyres and this made them hard to push if the wheels got into any ruts or into the spaces between the plank. To make things easier and better to handle, plates were laid so that the carts could run along them (66).

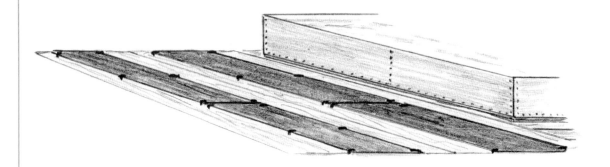

66 Metal plates laid so that carts could run along them

These plates were laid along the back end of the pans, right up to the door of the warehouse. It must not be forgotten that if there were only two men drawing a common pan, they would have to move the salt which they had drawn themselves. When all the salt had been moved off the hurdles the wallers would then wash them down. They would do this by filling the carts with water out of the bosh and letting it flush out as they wheeled it down the hurdle.

67 Pad worn to protect side of the leg

One thing that has not been said about the wallers is that when they were drawing a pan they would wear a pad on the leg that was the nearest to the rim of the pan. This was worn to protect the leg from rubbing on the rough plate.

This was made from an old piece of belting or a piece of old tyre (67).

The strings at the top were to tie onto the belt round the waist. The strings on the side were used to tie the pad to the leg.

The wallers' job starting around four o'clock in the morning would take them until between ten and eleven o'clock. They would then finish for the day.

At Winsford, the wallers like the lofters used to do the bagging of the salt, the lofters taking part in the bagging of the Lagos and the wallers doing the common and fishery salt. When the wallers were bagging the salt they would work in what was called a set, a set being three men working together. While one man used the shovel to fill the bags another would be holding the bag so that it could be filled and the other would weigh the bag after being filled and move it away from the scales on a truck.

If a big order was being done they would change over one man filling so many bags then he would hold so many and after that he would then go weighing and trucking away so that all the three had a turn at filling, holding and trucking away. So if there was an order for a hundred and eighty tons (182,880kg) four of five sets would bag this amount in the day.

Of course if there were bags being filled then there would have to be the bag stitchers there (69). These were the women who stitched the bags after they had been filled. As a rule the women who did this job years ago were widowed women and these, like the men, were paid on a piece work basis. Before the stitching machines came in these women also had to stitch the forty pound (18.144kg) white Lagos bags.

Apart from the wallers filling the bags and the women stitching them there would be another gang of three or four men trucking the bags away to be loaded into a boat. So here again was a busy scene that could have been seen in a salt warehouse, and although this was hard work there was very often jokes and laughter.

68 Wallers drawing a fishery pan

When the bag stitchers were stitching the bags in the warehouse they carried the string at their waist and a wooden sheath to keep their needles in. The sheath was made of wood and was hollowed out inside. This was packed with tallow. They used different sized needles for the different types of bags.

69 Bag stitchers in the warehouse

Most of these women also used to wear clogs often with ankle socks to protect their feet.

Of course, not to be forgotten are the bag medalers. These were the boys or men who put the metal seals on the bags after they had been stitched.

70 Bag seal   71 Detail   72 Seal from the Salt Union

The actual size of a bag seal one of these would be a little smaller than a present one pence piece. They were made of soft metal and were hollow inside. On one end there were two holes (70) and at the other one hole (71).

The two ends of string from the stitched bag were put one in each hole. These two ends then came out through the single hole. A couple of knots were put on which when pulled tight went inside the seal. The seal was then squeezed and the impression SU was left on it (72). When a boy or man was given this job he was said to be medaling the bags. All the bags used to have these on when they were shipped out.

Of course not all the salt went in bags. Quite an amount went in bulk and this would be loaded into the boats with the salt carts. When it was loaded in bulk a lot of effort would be made to keep it clean. The boat's hold would be washed out and any bare metal parts would be lime-washed. When the carts were being loaded a man or boy would be at each cart. He would pick any scale out and break any lumps up with a wooden mallet called a mor (73).

A mor was a block of wood with a stail in it. It was used to break the small lumps of salt up when salt was being loaded into the salt carts when bulk salt was being loaded. If someone did something silly on the salt works he could be called a 'mor yead'.

Also in the boat's hold there would be another man, or boy, picking any scale out that they could see. When the wallers were bagging the salt or putting it into the carts they would always just keep from putting any off the floor of the store-rus in case they got any dirt mixed in with it. So when any loading was going on one would always see a very thin carpet of salt under the feet of the wallers. This they would scrape up every so often and throw to one side.

73 A mor

Another thing that the wallers had to do when they were bagging or loading bulk salt was to get their own salt. When salt was tipped into a warehouse the first lot was tipped onto the floor. Then the salt that followed would be tipped onto the top of this and this would follow on over the weeks until the salt store was filled up.

This means that salt was tipped onto salt and by the time it was required for loading some of it, towards the middle of the pile, would have become quite solid. When they were bagging and they came to this it made extra work because they didn't get any extra pay for doing it. The tool they used for getting the salt was a salt pick.

The salt pick was a fairly slender pick and had a shaft about three foot six long (1m).

74 Salt pick

Sometimes they would have to dig right under the salt so as to get it to fall. There were occasions when they would have to use small paddles with stails in them about ten feet long (3m) so that they could get right under the salt. There were times when after they had cut under the salt they would have to go onto the top of the pile and drive big wooden wedges into it before the salt would break away. When this happened they had to keep an eye on the face of the salt, because the salt gave no warning before it would either slip down or roll over away from the face behind it. When a lump of salt rolled away from the face in a deep warehouse there would be quite a few tons of salt in it.

75 Beeswing shovel   76 Beeswing shovel cut back

The type of shovel that the wallers used was called a bees wing (75) and the wallers used this both for moving the salt and also for filling the two hundred weight and one hundred weight bags (102 and 51kg).

Sketch 76 is an old bees wing shovel with the blade cut short. When a shovel wore out it would be cut back by the blacksmith and would be kept for filling the smaller forty pound (18.114kilo) brown bags when they were filled with common or fishery salt for the African trade.

One of the things that one could see being put into the pan at a certain stage of the making of fishery salt was a few handfuls of alum. This was said to be put in to harden the salt. Another thing that was put in at a certain period was a bucket full of dolly blue. Dolly blue, which was in a block in a small bag, was used by the housewife in the days before modern washing powder to make white clothes whiter when she was washing. They said this was put into the salt pan to make the salt whiter.

Panboards were put into the pan at intervals during the making of fishery salt. These were two wooden boards which were nailed together so that they were stretched across the width of the pan. When they were made they were put together a little longer than the width of the pan so that when they were put in it they formed a slight bow which caused their ends to press against the side of the pan which therefore held them in position (77).

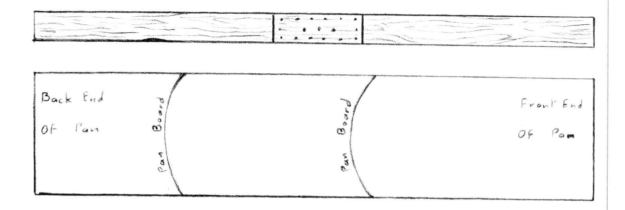

77 Panboard nailed together at the centre

They were made of lain seven by five eighths of an inch boards (180mm x 15mm). The lower sketch shows how the panboards looked when they were in the pan. The first was put in after a certain amount of salt had filled the back end of the pan. A second was then put in when the middle had filled.

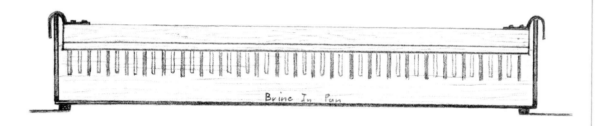

78 Panboards with pegs

Another type of panboard that was used with pegs was a three inch by three inch spar (76mm x 76mm) going the width of the pan. A seven by five eighths board (180mm x 15mm) was nailed to it. This was then bored so that three rows of pegs going the full length of the board could be knocked in. A cleat was then bolted on to each end of the spar so that these could rest on the rim of the pan holding the panboard in position (78). The board was then on the level with the brine in the pan and the pegs were lying underneath in the brine. The salt crystals used to fasten onto and around the pegs in quite big lumps. Both these type of panboard were used on the Birkenhead Works at Winsford.

Two more tools used on the Birkenhead Works were used to skim the soot and dust that used to settle on the surface of the brine.

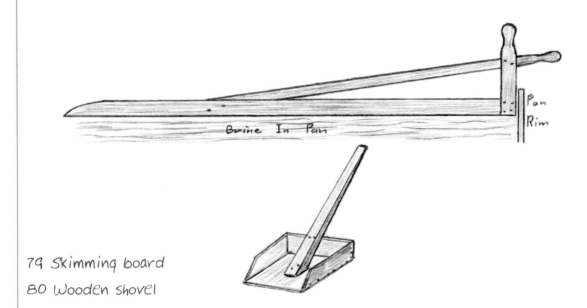

Brine In Pan

Pan Rim

79 Skimming board
80 Wooden shovel

Sketch 79 shows the tool that was used to skim the soot from the surface of the brine in the pan. It shows how it was held against the rim of the pan and then brought down the pan from the front to the back end. This skimming board was about ten feet long (3m) and had two handles on it. Sketch 80 shows the other tool that was used. This was a type of wooden shovel. After the soot and dust had been worked down to the backend of the pan this wooden shovel was used to lift it out of the pan. The job of cleaning off the top of the brine was always done the afternoon before the pan was drawn next day.

After the soot had been skimmed off, the hurdles on each side of the pan would then be washed down. It can be seen how particular they were and what efforts were made to keep the salt as clean as possible. The job of skimming the pan and washing the hurdles down was as a rule done by an old salt worker near to retiring age. He would also look after the rest of the pan yard and if anyone walked on the hurdles with dirty clogs after he had cleaned them up the language that came forth would be unprintable.

After the fishery pan had been drawn the cotter patches would be taken off and the brine would be emptied out of the pan. As a rule there would not be the thick scale that could have been seen on a lump pan in the fishery pan. But there would be a thin scale on the plate over the fires. Getting this scale off was as a rule done by one man who would be paid so much for the job using a picking or scaling hammer (81). This was not a very heavy hammer but having a fairly long stail he could strike the scale without having to bend his back as much as he would have had to do with a straight stailed hammer. Getting scale off was quite a hard job as it used to stick very firmly to the plate.

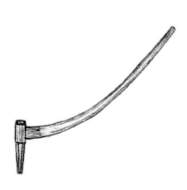

Having got some idea what a lumpmans, lofters and wallers jobs were like it can be said that these men worked hard and were not highly paid for doing it. Some old salt workers would say "Thee slogged thu guts ight fer next ter nowt."

81 Picking or scaling hammer

4 The Salt Makers, Lofters

Before describing the lofter's jobs let us look at the hothouse where he worked and its uses.

Firstly, when the lumpman fill the tubs on the dogs in the pan, the brine that is put into the tubs with the salt drains back into the pan through the slits in the bottom of the tub. When the tubs are lifted off the dogs onto the hurdle the brine is still draining through the bottom slits and through the hurdle. Even when the lumps are turned out of the tubs and are taken into the hothouses to be put into the ditches there is still a certain amount of brine in them. So it can be said that the hothouses are where the lumps finish draining and are dried.

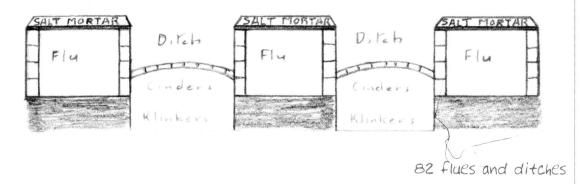

82 flues and ditches

The flue walls were built up with a metal plate across the walls and then salt mortar put onto the top (82). The ditch was dug out and filled with rough clinkers in the bottom, then rough cinders on the top of them and then fine cinders on the top. Onto the fine cinders were laid common brick which were put with a rounded surface. These were not laid tight together so when lumps were put into the ditch the brine that was left in them was able to drain away through the paving in the bottom of the ditch. Of course, over quite a number of years the ditch did gradually build up with salt under the paving. It also built up on the top of the paving with the wet lumps being put on them although the ditches were paddled and cleaned out every time the lumps are put onto the flues. The salt that accumulated on the paving was cleared out every so often and this was called yeowing the ditches.

Hothouses were not all the same size. Some were fairly long, others would not be as long and some of them were quite short. This of course would have something to do with where they were built and the space they had on which to build them. In some hothouses the ditches would take three lumps across and in some it would be found that the ditches would take four or five. In others the flues would only take one ditch of lumps on them and others would hold two ditches on one flue (83).

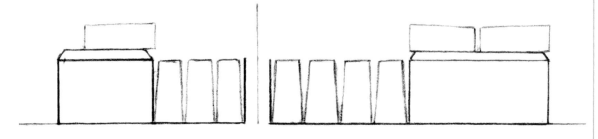

83 Lumps on the ditches

Some ditches were on a level with the floor of the hothouse, others were below the floor level.

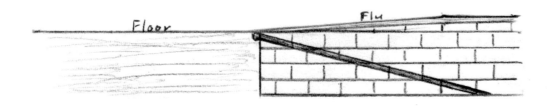

84 Ditch below the level of the floor

When the ditch was built below the floor level a short board was made so that the lumpman could get down into the ditch with his barrow. In the hothouses where this board had to be used the lumpman was paid a few coppers extra per shift and this was called plank money. So it can be seen how the different works had different ways of building the hothouses. Of course no matter which way they were built they were all used for the same purpose.

Having looked at the lumpman's job, how he did it and the hours he worked let us turn to the lofters job. The reason being that although the lofter did not actually work with the lumpman they did, in a way, work as a team.

After the lumpman had made his lumps he then put them onto his barrow and wheeled them into the hothouse and filled the ditches up. This is where the lofter started his job. It was his job to see that the lumpman always had room to put his lumps into the hothouse.

Like the lumpmen, the lofter's week would start early on a Monday morning. Most probably he would get to work the same time as the lumpman between three and four o'clock. The lofter wore the same clothes as the lumpman when he was doing his job, blue or grey flannels, but after the hothouses had got the heat on them he never wanted his shirt on.

For anyone who had never been inside a hothouse it could be a bit confusing because everything looked the same. The flues were there with the white lumps lying on them, also the ditches with the lumps standing in them, and you might think "Where do they start ?" because the flues were not numbered, neither were the ditches.

During the week, and taking a fair sized hothouse, the lumpman would fill all the ditches at least twice. Two ditches at a time were filled, which meant that the lumpman filled one ditch on each side of the hothouse and worked to the centre, filling the ditches from the outside to the centre ditches. If it had not been done like that the lumpman would have been running back and to across the hothouse and things could have got mixed up as well as getting the lumpman annoyed. So, starting on a Monday, the lofter would get onto the flue that had the lumps which had been put on about the middle of the previous week. He would throw the traps open that were in the ceiling over his head and start to put the lumps through it into the room above.

85 Lofting

There was only one lofter to each hothouse and he was responsible for the one in which he worked such as throwing the lumps up which were dry and taking the right ditches out. He also had to see that the lumps were put onto the flues right and make sure that the lumps were clean. Of course, in some works two lofters might work together and look after two hothouses between them. However, this was not always so as some preferred to work on their own. It will be noticed from Sketch 85 that the lofter has a tool in his hands with a lump of salt on the end of it. This tool was called a prong and this was only used by a lofter who was putting Lagos lumps into the room.

The prong had an ein about three feet long (90cm) with a kosp on one end and a spike on the other which was slightly curved. It was a tool which was difficult to handle as it could soon slip out of the lump. But once you got the knack of handling it, it was a very handy tool indeed.

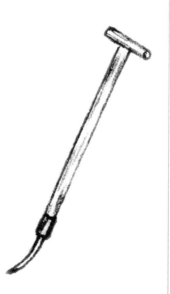

86 Prong

So, a Lagos lofter working on his own would use his prong and clear all the lumps under the traps. After he had cleared these he would then start to clear the lumps that were lying further along the flue under the room floor. This was where the prong was very useful because the lofter could reach the length of his arm and the prong, stab the prong into the lump and pull it towards him. Of course, he would have to go along the flue and throw a few back to the trap in which he was working and he would do this until he got halfway to his second trap. There would possibly be three traps along the length of the flue. After he had thrown his lumps into the room, he would brush all the bits of salt off the flue so as to clean it ready for the lumps that were going to be put on. Having brushed his flue off, he would then start to take the lumps out of the ditch and put these onto the flue, giving each lump a tap on the side to loosen it from the bottom of the ditch. If the ditch held three lumps across it, then the lumps would be three high on the flue. This was called ditching the lumps and when he had finished ditching them he would probably have put about three tons of lumps (3,048kg) onto the flue (87).

87 Ditching the lumps

When the lofter was ditching the lumps, on his hands he would wear a pair of hand rags. These as a rule were made from old woollen socks and were worn to protect the finger tips. If they were not worn the finger tips became very sore. Of course the toes of the socks were cut off. This was to stop any salt from collecting in the bottom of the socks because this would have made the fingers as sore as not wearing any protection.

Having ditched his lumps, the lofter would then get his scraper and start to scrape the bottom of the lumps as they lay on the flue (88). This was to take any bits of black off them that had got on while they were standing in the ditch.

88 Scraper   89 Paddler

The scraper, used for scraping the lumps, had a wooden handle and a steel blade about seven inches by three (177mm x 76mm). After he had scraped the lumps he would then get his paddle (89) and paddle the bottom of the ditch. The paddle that was used for getting the rough bits of salt from the bottom of the ditches had an ein about four feet long (1.2m) with a kosp and a steel blade about eight inches wide (20mm).

After he had paddled the ditch he would then brush it out and take the salt that he had brushed out to the soiled salt heap. How many flues he put into the room was up to him but it would be at least two or maybe three. Of course he would have to be sure that he kept ahead of the lumpman through the week. If he did not then the lumpman would be held up with his job. So that was how they, in a way, worked as a team.

Having finished his clearing up in the hothouse the lofter would then have to go up into the room above the hothouse because if he was working on his own he would have had to throw the lumps around the traps and he wasn't allowed to leave them like that. So he would go up into the room, drop the traps that he had opened and then he would start to stack the lumps up that he had thrown there. He would stack these about eight or nine high. After he had stacked them he would then brush the room up where the lumps had been lying and take that salt to the soiled salt pile and that would be his job for the day and by then it would be getting on for mid-day.

It should be explained that the Lagos lofters at Winsford also did the packing of the Lagos salt. This was called bagging the salt by the salt workers.

Of course the bagging was not done at the same works every day. So, whereas the lofter's day normally started at four o'clock in the morning and went on until noon, on the days when the salt was going to be ground and bagged they would start at two o'clock in the morning. This was because first of all they would have to throw the lumps off the flue and then take the lumps out of the ditch so as to make sure that the lumpman had room to put his lumps into the hothouse. They went in early like that so that they would be ready to start grinding and bagging the salt at seven thirty in the morning because the other workers would be there at that time such as the bag stitchers, the trucking gang and also the boat which was to take the cargo of salt would have been ordered there to load.

During the day they would most likely bag about one hundred and twenty five tons or so (127,000kg) and that would take them until late afternoon. The lofters job would be to feed the grinding mill with the lumps and also to fill the bags from the shutes.

So it can be imagined what long hours the lofters at the particular works would work during the day when the bagging was taking place.

90 Two wheeled lump cart

A low two wheeled lump cart was used in the rooms at Winsford to carry the lumps to the grinding mill. This was a flat bottomed cart and had raised shafts (90).

The scene in the room when the lumps were being ground in the mill was a scene of hustle and bustle - the lumps being loaded onto the carts and then being run to the mill, the lumps being put onto the belt which carried them to the top of the mill where they dropped inside to be ground up, the man filling the bags with the salt as they let it come out of the shutes, the bags being stitched, and the truckers loading their trucks and then taking them to be loaded into the boat that was taking the cargo of salt. It was certainly a scene of hard work and noise from the mill.

There was also a certain amount of colour when the white forty pound bags (18.144kilo) were being put up, with the blue, red and browns of the brands which were printed on the white bags. This certainly added some colour to the scene. There were the light brown ninety pounders (40.824kilo), also the packers. These were large bags filled with four or five smaller bags.

The salt when it went through the grinding mill was not ground up into fine salt. It could be said that it was broken up into small pieces. The people who bought this salt liked it in small lumps about as big as the end of the thumb. This was said to be nice and knobbly. They also liked a bag to be full to the top. If you felt a forty pound bag after it had been filled you would find that it was tightly filled and felt quite knobbly. Of course there was also a certain amount of small grains as well. Great care was taken to stop the white bags from getting any kind of marks on them. Small marks were quickly rubbed out with chalk. Great care was taken in the boat's hold. The long straw that could be got years ago was stood up along the bilges and curtains made of bags or berelap hung up the sides, Also the trimmers, the men who loaded the boats, had to wear canvas bags over their shoes.

Having had a look at the Lagos lofters it would be as well to have a look at the hand-it lofters job. In many ways it was the same as the Lagos lofter. They had to take the lumps off the flues and also the lumps out of the ditches and see that there was always room in the hothouses for the lumpman to put his lumps.

There were some differences in how this was done. The Lagos salt got its name because this salt was used for export to the different African countries, but the hand-it lump was made mainly for the home market. However, a certain amount of hand-it lumps were sometimes shipped across to Ireland. It makes you wonder whether the hand-it lump got its name from the fact that it was always moved by hand, whereas the Lagos lofters moved their lumps off the flues with a prong, the hand-it lofters always had to move their lumps with their hands. This was because a hand-it lump always had to be perfect and if a prong had been stuck into one, it would have been spoiled (91).

91 Hand-it lofters

When the hand-it lofters moved the lumps into the room above the hothouse they had to watch that they did not knock any of the corners off or break any pieces off at all. If this happened then the lump was thrown out as being no good for dispatching out. So it can be understood that these lumps were handled with care.

Besides taking the lumps off the flues and putting them up into the lump room some of the hand-its lofters would have to take the lumps off the flues with barrows. This was called running the lumps off. It should be explained that quite a lot of hand-it lumps went by rail and some works railway lines were put close to the hothouses so that the lumps could be loaded into the vans. Sometimes the lofters would load the vans themselves or others might run the lumps outside the hothouses and then the labourers would take them and load the vans.

92 Running the lumps off the flues

The barrows which were used to run the lumps off the flues would carry ten eighties which was about two and a half hundred weight (127.5kg). They had a wooden wheel with an iron hoop and were called dandy barrows. The tops of those flues were covered with salt mortar and the weight of those barrows running over it gives some idea of how hard salt mortar turns as long as it was kept dry and warm. Of course, they would also run along the ditches if one happened to be empty. Some lumps were wrapped up in paper, but most seemed to go unwrapped.

When they were shipped across to Ireland they were loaded into the boats at Winsford then taken to Liverpool and loaded into the ship there without any wrapping round them at all. They would have bagging or canvas put underneath them and over the top to help keep them clean. Here again you might say why not pack straw around them, but of course anything going to Ireland wasn't allowed to have straw around it from this country in case of any foot and mouth disease. This was the rule for bagged salt or lumps.

It might be asked what was done with broken lumps. Well of course lumps did get broken when they were being handled and there were orders for this type of salt in bags. It must not be forgotten that the hand-it lump was a smaller grained salt than the Lagos lump. When this type of salt was wanted in bags the lumps would be put into a grinding mill with sieves in it and this would go for orders of cheese salt and other sorts.

It will be seen that rather more trouble was taken with the hand-it lumps than with the Lagos lumps. After the lumps had been taken off the flues they would be brushed off and the lumps taken out of the ditches and moved onto the flues. They would be put onto the flues rather straighter than the Lagos lumps would be. After the lumps had been ditched the lofter would then get the watering can, this would be filled with brine or water and then the bottoms of all the lumps on the flue would be sprinkled. This was done so as to make the bottom of the lump soft. Of course, the hand-it lump was harder than the Lagos lump and more care had to be taken with the scraping of the bottoms of these lumps as they had to be level and neat. After the scraping had been done the ditch would be paddled. The paddling was done so as to cut away the bits and pieces that had got stuck to the bottom of the ditch and to keep it as level as possible. The ditch would then be brushed out and the salt taken to the soiled salt pile. The salt was called the dirty salt ruck by the salt workers.

What were the conditions of their work? Quite often they were rather bad. In some hothouses when you walked in the dry heat almost took your breath away and when the lumps were being thrown through the traps the salt dust would drop onto the lofters backs and into their hair. When it was very hot the sweat ran off your forehead carrying the salt dust into your eyes making things very painful. Not only that but the hothouses were very low and the lofters very often got their heads and shoulders bumped. Then there were the days when it was very humid and the sweat would pour out of the lofters before they had started to do any work. On other occasions if there were any cracks in the flues the hothouse would be filled with fumes from the fires. The lofter like the lumpman had to provide his own flannel and clogs and like the lumpman, the lofter drank quite an amount of tea and water.

How was the lofter paid? It was all piece work. He got paid for the amount of tonnage that he moved. The different types of lumps being paid at different rates. Like the lumpmen, they had their meal in the hothouse sitting on a lump, or on a salt tub or at the backend of the pan just outside the hothouse.

There was always one sound that could be heard in the hothouse and that was the sound of the crickets. In some hothouses they would be jumping out or in the way as the lofter went along a ditch taking the lumps out. So it can be said that the lofters job was quite often very unpleasant.

What has not been explained is how the lofters were paid when they bagged the Lagos salt. This of course was "a piece of work" job and they would be paid for the amount of tonnage that was bagged. However the bags were not all paid for at the same rate, the forty pounders (18.144kg) were paid at a different price than the ninety pounders (40.824kg) and the packers also at a different price to the other types of bags.

It may be of some interest to see how the lofters worked at Middlewich. At Seddon's Pepper Street Works the lofters worked in twos. Two lofters looked after two hothouses. When they were emptying the flues one would stand and throw the Lagos lumps up into the lump room and the other would stack them as they were thrown up, and then they would empty the ditches together. Of course the lofters at this works did not do the grinding and bagging of the Lagos the way they did it at Winsford.

At Seddon's Brooks Lane Works they had four hand-it lump pans and the four lofters here worked together as a team. Here again the hothouses were different. Two of the hothouses had a lump room above them and the other two did not. Of course, almost all the lumps at this works were run off the flues with the dandy barrows to be loaded into railway vans. On this works there was another firm named Simpson's. This firm did not make any salt itself but bought a great amount of hand-it lumps from Seddons and then sawed them up into smaller blocks with a circular saw. These were then wrapped in paper by the packing room girls. This firm also bought other types of salt which they packed. Seddon's Brooks Lane Works was one of the salt works where ditches which were below the level of the floor could be seen.

At Murgatroyd's Works in Brooks Lane there were four lump pans which made hand-it lumps and also lumps for grinding for the Africa trade. There were four lofters here and they worked as a team but there was also an extra man, who was not a lofter, but worked with them. He was called the cross trapper. He was not paid on tonnage, as the lofters were, but was paid an hourly rate his hours being from four o'clock in the morning to twelve noon. He was also employed as a hothouse man which means that he brushed the hothouses up and kept them as clean as possible. The reason they had an extra man with the lofters here was because the traps in the room floor did not follow along the flue the same as they did in most other hothouses, which means that when they started to empty a flue they would put the lumps through the first trap above the flue but when they came to the second trap this would be over the opposite flue. This was where the cross trapper came in. One lofter would stand on the flue that was being emptied, the cross trapper would stand in the ditch between the flue and where the trap was and this was the way the lumps were moved, passing them from one to the other. Another lofter would be up in the room stacking the lumps as they were passed up. The fourth lofter would be following up taking the lumps out of the ditch and putting them onto the flue. The lofters here did not take part in the grinding and bagging of the lump salt as they did at Winsford. This was also one of the works where the railway line ran close to the back of the hothouses so that if any railway vans wanted loading with lumps they could be run straight from the flues into them.

Another firm which took quite a lot of salt from Winsford was the Birkenhead Salt Company. They had a small dumb barge which used to load salt at Winsford, then carry it down the River Weaver, the Manchester Ship Canal and the River Mersey to the east float of Birkenhead Docks where it was used to discharge its cargo at the end of Cathgart Street.

5 Pansmiths and Firemen

The pansmiths were another body of men who worked hard and played a big part on the open pan salt works. These were the men who built the open pans and repaired them. They were also responsible for lifting the pans when they wanted repairing and lowering them when they had been repaired. When the pans were built, rings or hooks were fastened onto the rim plate of the pan, a lump pan having three on each side, or then more than three if it was a longer pan.

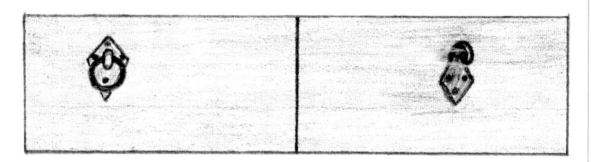

93 The hook, or ring, on the rim plate of the pans

Another piece of equipment needed to lift the pans was called a jigger and the jigger handle.

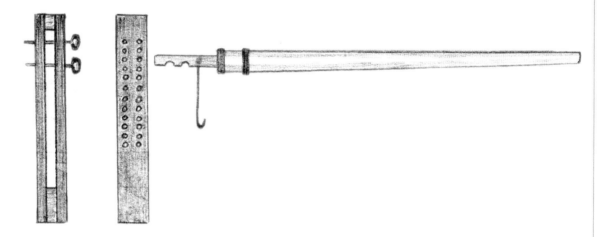

94 Jigger tool

The jigger was two pieces of steel with blocks between at the top and the bottom. Each side had a double row of holes which were lined up with the opposite side. This was done so that steel pins could be put through. The handle was also wood and steel. It will be seen that the steel end of the handle which went in between the sides of the jigger has two notches on the bottom edge. These were put in so that they corresponded with two steel pins which were pushed through. It can also be seen that there is also a steel hook. If the pan had a ring on the rimplate the hook would be put into it. If the pan had a hook on the rimplate then a ring would be used to couple them up.

95 Lifting the pan

When a pan was lifted the jigger would be put up to the pan with a piece of plank under its base. The handle would then be put in and hooked up to the hook or ring on the pan. The pins would then be put into the holes. The number of men inside the pan working the handle would be six at least and it would be easier if there were eight because as it can be seen from the sketch that they had to lift their own weight as well as the weight of the pan. The man standing outside the pan working the pins would give the order when to lift up or weigh down. So, the procedure would be that the man on the pins would shout "Lift up" When the men had lifted they must hold the handle in that position until the man on the pins shouted "In", which meant that he had got the pin into both the holes across from each other.

So that's what one would have heard when a pan was being lifted or lowered. "Weigh down", "In", "Lift up", "In". This procedure had to be strictly kept to, or someone might have got hurt.

The sketch shows one side of the pan but very often there would be a jigger on each side. When they had got the pan high enough to get a wooden block under they would then move to the middle of the pan to lift a bit there and then to the back end. And they would do this until they had got the pan as high as they wanted it. When the pan had been lifted high enough and the outside blocks were in place they would then go under the pan and put short props under it to take the sag out of the middle. They were not always picked up all round. Sometimes they would just lift one corner, or just lift the front end if it was just there where it wanted repairing.

96 A pan after it had been picked up at the front end

Blocks were placed under the pan and also the hooks on the side of the rimplate. All the plates in the pans were riveted together. If a bad plate had to be taken out all the rivet heads had to be cut off. This had to be done by hand and it was done by holding a sharp set against the rivet head and then giving it a few sharp blows with a heavy hammer. To be around a pan when the rivet heads were being cut off could be quite dangerous because the heads when they broke away travelled at a terrific speed. To stop this happening, the man who was holding the set would also have a stick with a piece of bag fastened on to the end of it. As he held the set to the rivet he would also put the stick with the bag on it onto the rivet head. This would stop it from flying away and therefore make it safer for the other men who were working near. If they had taken a plate out the next plate might want straightening out, so what they did was to get one or two shovelfulls of coals from the fires under the pan close by. They would put this fire onto the parts of the plate where it was wanted and when these parts had warmed up they would then straighten them out with the hammers. When they had measured up and found what size plate they wanted they would take the metal plate to the press. This was a machine that had a knife at one end to cut the plate and at the other end had a punch which punched the rivet holes in the plate.

97 Repairing and riveting a pan

When riveting a pan two pansmiths would sit on their low stools facing each other and striking down at the rivet head. The skill of these men sitting so close together and using these hammers as they whipped past each other setting up a rhythm which didn't change even when they changed their hands over on the shafts of their hammers was something worth seeing.

The job of the holder up was to hold the rivet in position with his holding up hammer while the rivet was being hammered down. He would be kneeling between the flue walls with the shaft of his hammer resting on a piece of wood across the flue walls. On the hurdle would be the rivet lad. He would have a portable fire in which he would heat the rivets.

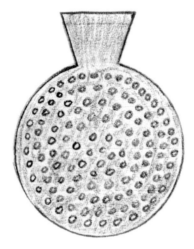

98 Skimmer

Another job the pansmiths could do was cutting plate to make skimmers. Sketch 98 shows a piece of plate cut out to make a skimmer. The holes punched in it would vary in size, large holes for coarse salt and smaller holes for finer salt. After it had been cut out it would be taken to the blacksmith so that it could be shaped and made so that the ein could be fitted on it.

A set (99) would have a green stick wrapped round the head and used for a shaft so that no shock would go up the arm of the person holding it when it was hit. A holding up hammer (100) had a shaft of about eight or nine feet (2.4m-2.7m) having a small round head on it . A riveting hammer (101) had a slightly curved shaft.

99 A set   100 Holding up hammer   101 Rivetting hammer

The men that must not be left out are the firemen. These were the men who fired the common and fishery pans. This was a hard and heavy job. These men were responsible for making the right type of salt in the pans which they fired. They had to see that they got as much salt as possible into the pans. This job as a rule was a shift job of twelve hours, working from four in the morning till four in the afternoon and from four in the afternoon till four in the morning. This would carry on through the week and then starting the following week the nightman would start on the day shift and the man who had been on the day shift would go on the night shift. As well as keeping the fires clean and seeing that they were well fired, they also had to see that the pans were kept well raked off over the fires so that the salt would not stick to the plate over the fires.

Their working clothes were the same as the lumpman, shirt (102), buskins (103), flannel drawers (104) and clogs (105) and like the others they had to provide their own.

Clogs were worn by most of the open pan workers because they lasted better than shoes. Maybe it should be mentioned that two well known clog makers were, in Winsford, Mr. Walker, and in Middlewich, Mr. Steel.

102 Shirt   103 Buskins

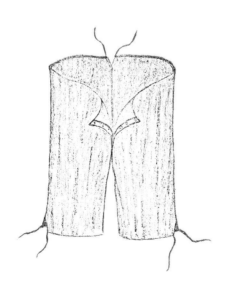

105 Clogs

104 flannel drawers

So here again were men who were important to the salt production on the open pan salt works.

The general labourers were employed on various jobs such as keeping the works tidy. When a pan had been lifted for a general repair they would work under the pan knocking the flue walls down and levelling it out ready for rebuilding and also yeowing the cats out. One might ask what is a cat under a pan. A cat was where a pan had been leaking through the plate. Over the weeks this would build up into a small mound of salt. In some cases this could block a flue up and with the heat being on it, it would set quite hard. Sometimes it would be hard to get out with a pick. So what they would do then would be to get a hosepipe and run water onto it for a few hours. This would dissolve part of it and make the rest simpler to get out. Some would have a job whitewashing round the panyard or store-rus. Others could be helping with the loading of a boat or some could be medaling the bags after they had been stitched. Then one would have a almost full time job as a 'ware-rus' or 'store-rus' man. His job would be to see that the warehouse floor was brushed up after the wallers had been bagging or loading bulk salt. If they were bagging salt they would set the scales out and put the correct weights on the scales and also see that one of the same type of bag that was being filled was put with the weights onto the scales. When the wallers had started bagging the salt he would also see that they were kept well supplied with bags till the order was finished. These were some of the jobs done by the labourers.

Another body of men that must not be forgotten are those who used to empty the wagons of coal that came onto the salt works. This was a dirty job and these were paid so much per wagon that they emptied. If it was a wagon that had traps in the bottom it could be emptied through these. This was the lowest paid. If they emptied it through the side traps then this was paid a little extra. If, however, it had to be all thrown over the side of the wagon then this was the highest paid. This was a job which had to be done in all weather and if it was a wet day then they would not only be soaked with sweat but rain as well. As well as emptying coal wagons these men also made up the trucking gangs. These had to truck the bags away after they had been filled with salt and stitched. They would truck them to the shutes when a boat was being loaded. This was all done at piece work rate. Another job they might do would be wheeling the ashes and clinkers away from the pans to the cinder tips. This was called mucking the pans. This job was paid at so much per pan. So here again were men who were poorly paid for their hard work.

One story used to be told about a young manager who, not knowing the salt works language, spoke to a man who he saw and asked him what he was doing. The man said "Am muckin." The manager said "Look here, my man. I want no cheek or you'll go up the road." The man said "A amner givin thee any chayk. Am a mucker, an am muckin theys pans." After a bit more argument the manager had to walk away a very puzzled man. He also left a puzzled man behind him because the man doing the job didn't know it by any other name. The name of the job in the office was ash wheeling.

6 Ancillary Trades and Life in the Salt Towns

The waste ashes and clinkers that were not wanted were disposed of from the open pan salt works in a variety of ways. In days gone by one would quite often see local farmers taking loads of ashes away with their horse and carts. It was a common sight to see these loaded carts going through Winsford. Hamlett's works who also had horses and carts used to take some of their ashes and tip them onto the filter beds which used to be on both the banks of the lower flash just above Winsford. Quite a lot of cinders and clinkers were used there both to build the filter beds and to keep the banks up at the side of the river. Any scale out of the pans used to be taken down to the loading stage at the side of the river and tipped into the water where it would wash away.

The Salt Union had quite a number of cinder tips on the side of the river. A very common sight on the cinder tips in days gone by were the cinder pickers. These were people who could not afford to buy coal. They would be there almost every day not only men, but women and children. They would have trucks made from a box with two wooden handles and old pram wheels and they would fill their bags with cinders and then load them onto their trucks to take them home.

The Salt Union used to have one or two wooden built hopper barges. These were boats with traps built into the bottom of them which could opened to let its cargo run out. These boats used to be loaded by what were called the cinder boat men. This was a gang of four men who were paid so much a boat. This again was a piece work job. Their job was to load the boat with the rubbish from the works such as old bricks, ashes, clinkers and scale from the pans. When they had loaded the boat a small steamer called *Pacific* would then tow the boat up to the lower flash above Winsford where the traps in the bottom would be lowered. The steamer would then tow the boat in a circle until all the rubbish emptied out. When the traps had been pulled up again the boat would then be towed back again to another cinder tip ready for loading the next day. When the salt works were not very busy, these men would not be wanted everyday so they would be off work.

The steamer *Pacific* was a small steam boat used by the late Mr. Malcolm who was called the "salt king". It used to take him to different salt works on the riverside that he wanted to visit at Winsford. It was manned by a crew of two, the captain who had been with the bigger boats and was finishing his time to retiring age, and an apprentice engineer who would start on this boat to get some experience of marine engines before going to the bigger boats.

The Salt Union also had two steam tugs. They were the *Firefly*, which was used in the River Weaver and towed the barges between Winsford and Marsh Lock or Weston Point Docks and which also towed the cinder boats up to the Winsford flashes after the Pacific went out of commission. The *Waterfly* was a more powerful tug which used to tow the barges between Winsford and Liverpool. This tug also at times would go into Liverpool Bay and tow a top sail schooner up the Mersey and the Manchester Ship Canal to Weston Point or Runcorn Docks.

The names of other steamers and barges that the Salt Union had for carrying the salt are too many to name and at one time of day must have been a very big figure. This was a job in which the men had to be very skilled. They would start loading their cargo in the morning and would sometimes be loading till five o'clock or after at night. They would leave Winsford and navigate through the night so as to be alongside the ship in Liverpool Docks to start discharging their cargo the next morning. This would be in all weathers, summer time and winter. Leaving

Winsford on a dark wet winter night and navigating the river without any lights wanted a bit of skill. The reason they were able to do this was because they knew the Weaver, the Ship Canal and the Mersey almost like the back of their hands.

Here again in this job the men had to provide their own equipment such as their own oilskins, their own bed, blankets, sheets for their bunks and also carry their own food with them. The only type of soap the firm supplied was a soft soap. As for the toilet facilities they would use a clean bucket or bowl which was supplied by the firm to wash in. As for the other part of the toilet they would throw a bucket over the side with a rope on, part fill it with water. They would then use it and throw the contents back into the water. The heating in the cabin was a coal fired oven and open fired grate, the coal, of course, provided by the firm, being carried in one of the lockers which formed the seating in the cabin.

While the boats are being looked at the trimmers should be mentioned. These were the men who stowed the bags in the boat's hold. This was a job that required quite a bit of skill because the bags had to be stowed so that there was no danger of any bags falling down when they were being discharged at the docks. This was a job that was paid at so much per ton and if things were slack in the salt trade and there wasn't any loading then they would not be working. Then there was the bag stopper. This man was one of the general labourers and it was his job to see that the bags as they came down the shute to the boat were kept under control. If this was not done then the trimmers stowing the bags could have been hurt.

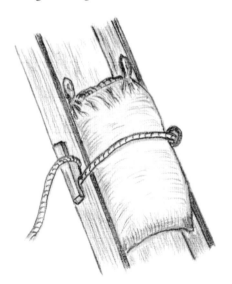

106 Bag stopper

Sketch 106 shows how the bag stopper kept the bags under control as they came down the shute to the boat. When he had stopped the first bag he would then let the following bags come to it. When he had got the weight of these he would then let the bags go through checking each one with the rope. This was a safety precaution that had to be used. The man would be standing close to the shute with ropes in his hands all the time.

There were ship carpenters at the dockyard at the Meadow Works. Their job was to keep boats in good repair. At the dockyard there was also a well kept sawmill which had circular band and also a steam saw for cutting the tree trunks up. A lot of the timber that was used on the boats and on the salt works was cut at the dockyard sawmill. The wood used for making the tubs for the lump pans was also cut there. If quite a large number of salt tubs were wanted for one of the saltworks then at different times the ship carpenters would make them. The small boats that were carried by the river craft were also built here.

At the dockyards were also the sailmakers. These men made all the tarpaulin covers that were used to cover the hatches on the boats. They also spliced the wires that were used on the winding gear on the steamers. They also carried out the inspections of this gear to see that it was always in good condition.

The dockyard blacksmiths used to anneal the chain shrouds and see that there were no cracks in any of the links. The shrouds or mast stays on the Salt Union boats were all chain link, not wire as on other firms boats. They also did other smith jobs that were wanted at the dockyard.

On the Meadow Island there was the fitting shop. The engineers here also looked after the engines, the boilers and the winches on the boats and saw that these were kept in good running order. This was where the boats had the boilers scaled and cleaned. Some of the boats had their boilers scaled every six weeks and some every three months.

At times the management at the Salt Union were very keen on time management. This happened one day in May in 1929. In those days a steam buzzer that could be heard all over Winsford used to be blown. This buzzer used to be blown at twenty-five past and half past seven in the morning, at twelve noon and one o'clock and also as five o'clock in the evening. On this particular day the men were ready to knock off at twelve noon. The buzzer blew and a fifteen year old boy, working in the joiners shop, which was fairly close to the clock office dashed out of the joiners' shop on his push bike, clocked off and went home for his dinner, came back at one and finished the day. The next morning the Works' Manager came to the joinersí shop, gave the boy a good ticking off and told him that he was suspended for three days. This was called getting grest on the salt works. What the boy hadn't known when he dashed on his bike to clock off, was that Mr Malcolm had been standing and watching through his office window. He asked for the clock cards to be sent to him. The time stamped on the card was one minute past twelve. The boy and a general labourer had both got this time on their cards. Both of them were suspended for three days without pay. The reason being that Mr Malcolm said that a man could not get from his job to the clock in that short space of time. I remember this tale because I was that fifteen year old boy.

The salt works' joiners were men who always had a job to do seeing that the hurdles and roofs were kept in good order. If on a works with lump pans they would make new salt tubs. The joiners also made the box barrows and the salt carts. Not only did they make these but they would also make the wheels to go with them. When these wheels had been made they would then take them to the blacksmith to have the metal tyres put on. The blacksmith also had plenty of jobs to do making or repairing tools that were used on the works and was like the other tradesmen, essential on the salt works.

Then there were men in the central stores at Winsford. This storeroom was on the river bank between Birkenhead Works and the Uplooant Works. It was to this stores the bags were brought that would be later filled with salt. Here everything would be counted. There was also a printing machine here that was used for printing the lettering or brand marks that were put onto the bags. There was no colour printing here just black ink. There was also a printing machine at the National Works lower down the river.

Then there were the shunters. These were the men who shunted the wagons in and out of the works. These were the men who worked the 0-4-0 saddle tank engines which were often called the dumpy engines. They would bring the wagons of coal in and put them in different pans where they were to be emptied. The shunters would also place the empty wagons where they were wanted for loading with salt and later they would marshal them all together for the main line engine to pick them up. These engines were on the different works at the Salt Union. At the Meadow Works at Winsford in the early twenties a horse was used to move the wagons about but this job was later taken over by a tractor. A steam engine was also used at Murgatroyd's open pan works at Brooks Lane, Middlewich for shunting. A wagon of coal on a salt works was called a 'slek wagin', or a 'wagin a slek' and water was called 'weetu' or 'wartu'. At Birkenhead Works at Winsford when the engine was doing the shunting jobs a flag lad was to be ahead of the engine at different crossings or danger points holding his green or red flag out whichever would be wanted. Other men that had always plenty of work to do were the wagon builders and repair men. Most open pan salt works employed these men both at Winsford and Middlewich.

An important job done by a teenager at Winsford was the boat lad's job. This boat was a flat bottomed square ended heavy built thing and it was propelled by a single oar, which means it had to be sculled across the river. It was stationed at the bottom end of the Meadow Island which was the farthest point from the entrance to these works. This boy's job was to carry any of the workers across the river from the Wharton bank to the Meadow, or from the Meadow to what was called the Woodend side which was the opposite side of the river. This was very often a busy job and when the river was in spate in the winter it was very hard work. It was a service that was very important because if the boat had not been there many hours would have been lost because the workers would have had to walk to Winsford Bridge to get across or down to the National Works which was almost at Meadow Bank where there was a boat without a boy to scull across.

Another job that many did not know about was the order lad's job. When the lofters had done their job for the day at Winsford Salt Union they would go home between eleven and twelve o'clock. They would then come to work at their normal starting time the next day. However, if an order came in the afternoon for a cargo of Lagos salt to be ground and loaded the next day then the order lad would go round to their different homes and tell the lofters what the orders were for the next day such as the number of tons that had to be loaded. They would then know what time they had to start the next morning. The boy would do this after he had finished work at five o'clock in the evening and he would be paid an hours overtime for doing this.

The man in charge of the different open pan salt works must not be forgotten. In the early days he was not called works foreman but the bonksmun (banksman).

With some types of open pan salt it was a kind of stop-go trade. The Lagos salt would be going winter and summer but some of the fishery and common would be slack in the winter and not start to go till early summer. The Montreal trade would be shipped out from early summer till the autumn and then this would stop. What little did go in the winter would go to Halifax, Canada. Hundreds of tons of salt for the fishing industry trade would be shipped from Winsford to Weston Point Docks in the autumn but then this trade would stop in the autumn. So in days gone by if some of the warehouses had got filled up while the trade was slack then the wallers would be out of a job. There were tales told by the very old salt workers that in days gone by that when they were out of work because the salt trade was slack, when the salt started to go again the banksman from different salt works would come to them when they were standing in Winsford and almost go down on their knees asking the men to come and work for them at their works. Of course there must have been a shortage of men at sometime because men were brought over from the continent to work at the salt works. That is the reason the bass houses were built at Meadow Bank to house these men.

So this was the salt trade in days gone by. Sometimes too many men and other times not enough to do the work to get the salt moving again.

Having had a brief look at most of the workers who worked on the salt works it might be asked how did they get to and from work. The answer is, by using shanks's pony, which means by walking. The workers used to think nothing of walking three or four miles each way and some would walk farther. There would be some who had a push bike but it was considered something if one owned one of these. So the sound that could be heard was the clatter of steel tipped clogs as the workers went to the jobs and this sound could be heard very early in the morning as the lumpmen, wallers and lofters were going to work. It was possible to almost tell the time by the sound of some of the workers going past and most of the men would be carrying the small wicker baskets that used to be quite common in those days for carrying their dinner in and also the different size cans that they would carry their tea in. Others would carry their dinners in a red handkerchief. This was another common sight because most working men used a red handkerchief in those days. These had different patterns on them from white spots to white lines round the hems. Another common sight in those days would be the men with quite a number of patches on their overalls and on a Monday morning you would see well patched, spotlessly clean overalls.

107, 108, 109 Tea can, basket and kerchief

Figures 107, 108 and 109 give some idea of what the small wicker basket looked like with the lid fastened at the side and on the lid, coloured white, blue or brown. Also what the red handkerchief looked like knotted at the top.

How did people spend their leisure hours? Well, men liked a pint of beer. There were quite a number of public houses in what was called the bottom of Winsford. This was a few hundred yards each side of the bridge. Of course there was more home life in those days. One reason being that people hadn't the money for anything else. There was no wireless or television either so how would they spend the winter evenings? The housewife would no doubt be darning socks or patching overalls, or maybe making clothes for the children for there was a lot of this done in those days. There were also a lot of patchwork quilts made for the beds. These were made by stitching different pieces of coloured cloth together, or maybe they would be knitting socks.

The women of those years always seemed to be busy especially if they had any family. The husband might go out for a pint if he could afford it. A pint of beer did a man good if he had been sweating on the salt works. If he didn't go out for a drink he might be making a cloth rug. A lot of these were made. Most of the working class houses that you went into would have a cloth rug on the floor in front of the fire. These were made by getting a piece of sacking then cutting short strips of old cloth up and then pegging these into the sacking. Some used to make some very fancy patterns in them with coloured cloth. Or of course if he had a family he might be doing a bit of mending. These are just a few of the things that would possibly be done in a working class house.

After the children had their tea would very likely be out playing in the streets. They would be playing around or what they called playing under the lamp close to home. They were all gas lamps then and they would play here until they were called in to go to bed. The boys of the family if they had started work and had got an apprenticeship might possibly be out at night school. The apprentices at the Salt Union had to go to night school two nights a week.

Entertainment in Winsford was fairly mixed. There was the Drill Hall in Dingle Lane where dances used to be held at different times. This was later turned into a theatre called the Hippodrome where one could see variety acts. Then around 1920, a new cinema was built in Weaver Street. This was called the Magnet Cinema. Later, the Super Cinema was opened in the market place. Of course there were a number of dances held in the church schools also concerts at different times by local concert groups.

On a Saturday there was a local football team playing in the Cheshire League. Also on a Saturday there was the market in Winsford, the stalls standing in the street from Winsford Bridge to where the old fire station was (this being on the opposite side of the road to the present one). On a Saturday night this part of Winsford used to be full of people standing around the crockery and clothing stalls and the stall where they sold the local swaggering dick and humbugs. Quite a number would always be there selling their different remedies. Of course there wasn't the road traffic in those days. There was no bus service between different towns. If anyone wanted to go to Northwich they had to go from the Cheshire Lines station in New Road and no trains left there on a Sunday.

More people used to go to church or chapel in those days and most of these places used to have very good choirs. On Saturday and Sunday nights on each side of the road through Winsford from the top of High Street to the fire station the teenage boys and girls would be seen chatting to each other in groups making it difficult at times for the older people to get through. But there was rarely trouble, most of them being very well behaved and quite a number of Winsford lads met their wives of the future here. The children went to the different schools and in those days it was no disgrace to go to school in a pair of clogs and there were few school uniforms seen apart from those who went to the grammar school. Some of the schools would have very good mixed choirs and during the summer singing competitions would be held where not only Winsford school choirs would compete but choirs from schools outside the town also.

There were few that could afford to go on summer holidays. The children would spend their days playing out in the fields and some of the boys, after the local baths had been burned down, would go swimming in the flashes and that is where a lot of Winsford lads learned to swim. The grown ups of course had their sport as there were quite a number of bowling greens in Winsford and there used to be quite a lot of fishing done in the flashes and the river.

There was also a lot of walking out in the summer. On a Sunday afternoon there would be lots of people walking along the flash banks and also sitting on the grass. Stonely's and Breeze's boats could be hired out at so much an hour so that some would have a few hours boating. The boat people used to have motor boats which would take people up the flashes and there were plenty of picnics had on the banks of the flashes. The farmers who farmed the land were very lenient.

The children that went to church Sunday Schools would have what they used to call the Sunday School Treat. If they went to St Chads Church in Over the children going to the treat would all assemble at Darnhall School where they would be put onto a horse drawn lorry with the side rails on and they would be taken by this lorry to Darnhall Hall where they would have their day out. The parents would walk behind following the lorry. From the Wharton side of town some would go to Bostock Hall. In later years when local men bought the open charabancs, one of the first being a Mr Stubbs who had a garage on the left hand side of High Street hill, and the different schools used to take the children on trips to the sea-side. There used to be a lot of local amateur football teams with very keen competition between them as well as local cricket teams.

Quite a lot of travelling fairs came in days gone by. One fair used to be at the back of the Red Lion Hotel for weeks on end. This was Royal's Fair. Other fetes were also held and there was also the September Fair at the Four Lane Ends. This was held on a piece of ground that was Birtwistle's shop. The Co-op and the bank were then built on it. Some used to call it the Onion Fair. When this was held all the apprentices at the Salt Union were given a shilling each and half a day off to go to the fair. The boys who worked with the general labourers were not given this, neither the boys who were serving their time on the boats. There seemed to have been a bit of class distinction there.

So there it is, the salt works and the people who worked on them. People who worked hard for little money, but who did the best they could in the circumstances.

Tom Lightfoot, 1914 to 1996

Tom Lightfoot was born in Winsford in 1914 and lived there all his life. He went to Gladstone Street School, though according to him, he was "not much of a scholar". The town he knew in his childhood was dominated by the salt industry so that the salt works and boats on the River Weaver were very familiar to him long before he left school.

When he left school at fourteen he was taken on by the Salt Union to work in the joiners' shop at the Birkenhead Salt Works. This was but one of many works which at that time lined both banks of a two mile stretch of the river between Town Bridge and New Bridge.

When he was sixteen he became an apprentice on the boats and served his time with the Salt Union packet *Albion* and the barge *Charles*. At the end of his time, in 1935, he had to leave the Salt Union as there was no job for him and he went to George Hamlett and Sons, one of the few remaining independent firms at Winsford, working as a mate on the *Premier* and the *Prince of Denmark*.

In 1939 he joined the salt firm of Henry Seddon and Sons of Middlewich and worked on the barge *Gowanburn*. He left the river in 1950 so that he could spend more time with his family and worked on the salt pans at Seddons Works, Middlewich. But he still continued to make the occasional trip down the river as mate on Seddon's two boats, the packet *Weaver Belle* and the barge *Gowanburn*.

It was only in 1955 that he left the river for good when he joined Murgatroyd's Salt Works in Brooks Lane, Middlewich where he remained until his retirement in 1976. Although the open pan works on this site closed down in 1966, and was demolished in 1968, this was the location of the brine pumping station which supplied brine to the vacuum salt and chlor-alkali brine electrolysis plant three miles away at Elworth.

It was in 1974, whilst working as Senior Brine Pumpman at Murgatroyd's, that he produced this detailed account of salt making drawn from his observations and experiences gathered during a working life spent in the industry.

Tom showed a remarkable memory for detail and in this text records the way of life and working practices of the Cheshire salt workers.

GD Twigg September, 2000

Notes on the Text

The original text and illustrations which form the basis of this book were written in long hand by Tom Lightfoot with the support and encouragement of Lady Rochester and George Twigg. Both George Twigg and Lady Rochester had endeavoured to save documents and artefacts of the dying open pan salt industry of which the Lion Salt Works, a family business, became the only survivor. They worked to re-open the Northwich Salt Museum which had been established by Sir John Brunner in 1889 but always felt that the preservation of mere objects and pieces of paper did not adequately explain the technical skills used in the production processes. In Tom Lightfoot they found a willing author who developed his own style to describe the tools and practices with which he had grown up.

George Twigg would aid and prompt his records providing a supply of pencils and lined paper. The result is almost a written conversation which we hope is retained in this edition. Pages would be worked on until an accurate and fair copy was produced. Each page incorporated the drawings and the text, making re-writing a time consuming business.

Lady Rochester edited Tom's memoirs of working on the Weaver boats and published 'The Weaver Watermen' in 1983. At that time the text describing the open pan salt works was put to one side possibly because the Lion Works was still operational and provided practical demonstrations of how salt was made by open pan evaporation.

The Lion Salt Works eventually closed in 1986 and through the support of Vale Royal Borough Council a Trust was established in 1993 to restore it as a working industrial museum. Lady Rochester became a founder Trustee and shortly after Tom's death in 1996 she and George Twigg drew the Trust's attention to the unpublished manuscript. Sadly, Lady Rochester herself died before it could be published.

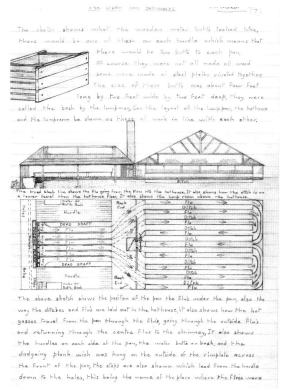

Editing has involved three basic tasks, removing the blue lines from beneath the pencil sketches, removing repetition and reorganising some of the sections so that the processes can be followed by readers unfamiliar with salt making. After reading the account we hope, to quote Tom's style, that 'having seen the way in which the open pan salt works were built, and the men who worked in them, that you will understand how the salt was made'.

Illustration 1 - A page from the original manuscript

List of Illustrations

Maps

Photographs

Illustrations

Index